Contents

Introduction:
Your Adventure Begins Here!

First off, let's begin with a hearty welcome! You've taken a bold step into the thrilling world of algebra 1 by picking up this book. We're about to embark on an exciting journey together, where we'll unravel algebraic mysteries and crack complex codes, all while navigating strange lands and meeting fascinating characters.

This isn't your typical math book. Instead of pages filled with equations and theory, you'll find stories packed with adventure, suspense, and (yes, you guessed it!) math. We've carefully woven algebraic concepts into each tale, making learning as fun as it is effortless.

Math Is Everywhere

Have you ever wondered why we need to learn algebra? Well, you might be surprised to learn that math is all around us! It's in the food we eat, the music we listen to, the games we play, and even the nature we admire. In this book, we'll see how the abstract concepts of algebra come to life in real-world situations, helping you connect what you're learning with your everyday life. So keep an eye out—you'll start to see math everywhere!

How to Use This Book

Read, Re-Read, and Reflect

Each chapter in this book presents a new algebraic concept framed within an intriguing story. Don't rush through! Take your time, and try to visualize the story as it unfolds. Remember, it's not just about the destination, but the journey too!

After your first reading, take a moment to reflect on the story and the math concept it introduces. Then, re-read the chapter. You'd be surprised how many new details you'll pick up on a second reading. Remember, understanding and mastering a new concept takes time and practice, so don't worry if you don't grasp it immediately.

Practice Makes Perfect

At the end of each chapter, you'll find a 'Chapter Review' section filled with important concepts, sample problems, and solutions. This is your personal workout space! Use it to flex your math muscles and practice what you've learned. The more you exercise, the stronger you'll become.

Keep Coming Back

Think of this book as your algebraic time machine. You can revisit any chapter, any time, for a refresher on a particular topic. The concepts you'll learn are not stand-alone; they're interconnected, much like the chapters in our adventure. So, if you're studying a topic at school and you need a little extra help, don't hesitate to come back and re-read the corresponding chapter.

You're Ready!

Remember, math, like any subject, becomes easier and more enjoyable the more you engage with it. So, read the stories, solve the problems, and above all, have fun with it!

Remember, our aim is not just to learn algebra but to enjoy the learning process. So don't be afraid to let your curiosity guide you. Ask questions, seek answers, and don't forget to have fun. After all, algebra is not just about solving equations—it's about unlocking a new way of thinking about the world. So, fellow adventurers, let's start our journey and, as they say in the world of algebra, let the numbers do the talking!

CHAPTER 1

Welcome to Numeria High

The town of Numeria was quaint, charming, and had an odd quirk—it was positively obsessed with numbers. Street names were based on mathematical constants, the local diner offered a 'Fibonacci special' with a peculiar number of fries, and Numeria High, the town's only school, was renowned for its remarkable math curriculum.

Our story begins on a sunny Tuesday in Numeria High. The school was a unique blend of old and new—classic brick walls with high-tech smart boards in every classroom. The hallways echoed with laughter, whispers about weekend plans, and yes, the occasional groan about an algebra assignment.

Enter our heroes—three diverse yet inseparable friends who made up the unlikeliest of math teams. First, there was Mia, a bright, bubbly girl with a head full of curly hair

and a heart full of curiosity. She had a knack for making friends with just about anyone—students, teachers, even the grumpy old janitor. Mia loved math, not because she was particularly good at it, but because it was like a puzzle, a tantalizing mystery waiting to be solved.

Next, there was Leo. Leo was a thinker, the quiet, contemplative type. With his glasses perpetually perched on his nose and a book always within reach, he was the go-to guy for any math problem that had the rest of the class stumped. But, despite his intellect, Leo was humble and always willing to lend a helping hand.

Finally, there was Priya. Priya was the creative spirit of the trio. A gifted artist, she saw the world in vibrant colors and unique patterns. While math wasn't her first love, she appreciated its symmetry and structure, and she had an uncanny ability to visualize complex mathematical concepts.

The three friends, united by their shared math class and their knack for stumbling upon mysteries, were about to embark on their greatest adventure yet—an adventure that would transform their understanding of algebra, challenge their problem-solving skills, and bring them closer together. Little did they know, the mystery of the missing variable was about to unfold.

CHAPTER 2

The Algebraic Artifact

The day had started off just like any other at Numeria High. Morning classes had been a blur of note-taking, presentations, and the usual pre-lunch anticipation. As the lunch bell rang, students flooded into the hallways, chattering and laughing.

Mia, Leo, and Priya sat at their usual spot in the cafeteria, a corner table by the window. As they unpacked their lunches, Mia couldn't help but feel a sense of excitement. Today was the day their math teacher, Mr. Euler, was rumored to reveal a mysterious artifact linked to their algebra unit.

As the friends discussed their anticipation, Priya suddenly looked up from her sketchbook. "You know," she said, her eyes sparkling with mischief, "we could sneak into the classroom and take a peek before anyone else."

Leo, always the voice of reason, shook his head. "That's against the rules, Priya."

But Mia was already nodding, her eyes alight with curiosity. "Let's do it," she said, standing up. "Adventure awaits!"

Laughing, they left their half-eaten lunches and snuck off towards Mr. Euler's classroom. The school was quieter now, the hallways empty. As they rounded the corner, the trio slowed down, their footsteps echoing in the silence. With a shared look, they pushed open the door to Room 314.

The room was empty, the smart board dark, the desks neatly arranged in rows. But on Mr. Euler's desk was a cloth-covered object—the artifact. Mia looked at Leo and Priya, her eyes wide. "Should we...?"

Before she could finish her sentence, Priya had already reached out and pulled off the cloth. Underneath was a box. It was old and worn, but in its center, there was a bright, silver lock. Inscribed on the lock were strange symbols—mathematical symbols.

"This must be it!" Mia exclaimed, her voice a hushed whisper. She traced the symbols with her fingers. "But how do we open it?"

As they looked at the box, Mia, Leo, and Priya noticed that the symbols inscribed on it were similar to what they had recently learned in their pre-algebra class. There were numbers, variables, and even an equal sign.

Leo, who had been observing quietly, adjusted his glasses and stepped forward. "These symbols... they're not just any symbols. They're algebraic symbols."

"This looks like an equation," Leo said, adjusting his glasses and leaning in for a closer look. "See, here's a '2', and an 'x', and it's equal to '6'." He wrote down the equation on a piece of paper: $2x = 6$.

"You're right," Mia said, her eyes lighting up with understanding. "And I think I remember Mr. Euler teaching us about something like this. We have to isolate 'x', the variable, right?"

Leo nodded. "Yes, exactly. We need to perform the same operation on both sides of the equation to keep it balanced. So, we can divide both sides by 2." He quickly did the calculation: $x = 3$.

The three friends excitedly tried the solution on the lock, turning the dial to '3'. To their surprise, they heard a soft click, and the box sprang open.

Inside was a note. It read: "Congratulations! You've unlocked the first step in understanding the world of algebra. The mystery of the missing variable awaits you."

The trio looked at each other, a mix of excitement and anticipation on their faces. Their algebra unit was going to be more interesting than they had ever imagined.

Just then, the bell rang, signaling the end of lunch. Startled, they quickly replaced the cloth and hurried out of the classroom, their hearts pounding. As they made their way back to the cafeteria, they couldn't help but grin at each other.

The rest of the school day was a blur. They couldn't concentrate on their afternoon classes, their minds filled with algebraic symbols and the promise of an intriguing mystery.

When the final bell rang, they were the first ones out of their classrooms, rushing towards Room 314. Mr. Euler was already there, standing by his desk, the cloth-covered box in front of him. He looked up as the trio burst into the room, a knowing smile playing on his lips.

"I see we have some eager students," he said, his eyes twinkling.

The rest of the class trickled in slowly, chatting and laughing. Finally, when everyone had settled down, Mr. Euler lifted the cloth off the box, revealing the silver lock and the algebraic symbols. A hush fell over the room.

"This," Mr. Euler began, "is an ancient artifact. It's a box that can only be opened using the principles of algebra. It's been passed down from mathematician to mathematician, each one adding their own puzzles and challenges."

After revealing the box, Mr. Euler began the day's lesson. "Algebra," he started, "is like a puzzle, much like this box. It's all about finding the value of unknowns—what we call variables."

He turned to the board and wrote '3x = 9'. "Here," he explained, "x is our variable. It's what we don't know. Our job is to find its value."

He looked at the class, his eyes scanning over the curious faces. "So, how can we find the value of x?"

A few hands shot up, and Mr. Euler nodded at a student in the front row.

"We can divide both sides by 3," the student said.

"Excellent!" Mr. Euler praised, writing out the steps on the board, '3x/3 = 9/3', which simplified to 'x = 3'. "And that's the essence of algebra," he said, pointing to the final equation. "It's about maintaining balance. What we do to one side of the equation, we must do to the other."

As the class progressed, Mia, Leo, and Priya each took turns solving different equations on the board, their confidence growing with each correct answer. They applied the same principle again and again, gradually getting accustomed to the rules of algebra and its language. They saw how changing the operation or the numbers influenced the variable's value.

The rest of the class followed along, the initial apprehension slowly replaced by understanding. Algebra wasn't so intimidating after all. It was a systematic process, a step-by-step method to find the missing variable.

By the end of the class, the trio felt a sense of accomplishment. They had not only unlocked a physical box but also the beginnings of the algebraic world. As they left the classroom, they were eager for the next lesson, the next piece of the puzzle. They were ready to dive deeper into the mystery of the missing variable.

CHAPTER 2 OVERVIEW

Concepts Covered

- **VARIABLES:** In algebra, variables are symbols used to represent unspecified numbers or values.
- **EXPRESSIONS:** An expression is a combination of variables, numbers, and at least one operation like addition or subtraction.
- **EQUATIONS:** An equation is a statement that two expressions are equal, such as $7 + x = 10$.

Practical Applications

Understanding variables, expressions, and equations is the foundation of algebra. They are used in various real-life situations, such as calculating distances, determining quantities, and solving problems. In this chapter, our adventurers used the understanding of variables and expressions to decipher a code and open the algebraic artifact.

Key Equations or Formulas

An example of an equation from this chapter is $3x = 9$. In this equation, 'x' represents a number, and the equation is solved when 'x' equals 3.

Practice Problems

1. Simplify the following expression: $3x + 2y - 4x + 5y$.
2. Solve the equation: $2x - 7 = 15$. What is the value of 'x'?
3. Solve the equation for z: $z / 2 = 6$
4. Solve the equation for a: $3a = 21$
5. If the cost of a book is $12 and you buy 'b' number of books, express the total cost as an algebraic expression.

Solutions

1. Combining like terms, we have $(3x - 4x) + (2y + 5y) = -x + 7y$.
2. Adding 7 to both sides, we get $2x = 22$. Dividing both sides by 2, we find $x = 11$.
3. To solve for 'z', we multiply both sides of the equation by 2. This gives us $z = 6 * 2$, so $z = 12$.
4. To solve for 'a', we divide both sides of the equation by 3. This gives us $a = 21 / 3$, so $a = 7$.
5. The total cost would be 12b, which is the cost of one book multiplied by the number of books.

CHAPTER 3

Unraveling the Mystery

The next morning, Mia, Leo, and Priya entered Room 314 with a strong sense of anticipation. It was different from the usual pre-class jitters. This time, they were eager. They were on the brink of an adventure, and it all started in their algebra class.

As they settled into their seats, they noticed Mr. Euler preparing something at the front of the room. He wasn't at the smartboard as usual, but at his desk, a sense of excitement dancing in his eyes. He was carefully unfolding a large, worn-out piece of parchment. The edges were yellowed with age, and the intricate drawings and symbols that decorated the paper hinted at its importance.

The room fell silent as everyone's attention was drawn to the front. Mr. Euler cleared his throat, bringing the anticipation to a peak. "Good morning, class," he began, his voice filled with a mystery that matched the atmosphere in the room. "Today, we're not just going to learn about algebra, we're going to live it."

He gestured to the paper in front of him. "This," he announced, "is a map to a hidden treasure. A treasure that was hidden by a legendary mathematician who loved algebra and believed that understanding it was a key to unlocking the world's wonders. He hid his greatest discovery and left behind this map filled with algebraic clues."

A wave of whispers swept through the class. The prospect of a treasure hunt turned the typical classroom chatter into an electrifying buzz. Algebra wasn't just numbers and variables anymore—it was the key to a real-life treasure.

Mr. Euler quieted the class and moved to the smartboard. He wrote an equation on the board: 5x - 3 = 7. "To find our first clue, we need to solve this equation for 'x'. Remember, our goal is to isolate 'x', keeping the equation balanced."

Leo was the first to raise his hand. His analytical mind was already at work. "First, we should add 3 to both sides to cancel out the '-3' on the left side," he proposed.

"Excellent start, Leo!" Mr. Euler praised, making the adjustments to the equation on the board, which now read 5x = 10.

Mia, her mind as sharp as a tack, quickly saw the next step. "Now, we can divide both sides by 5 to find the value of 'x'," she suggested.
"Brilliant, Mia!" Mr. Euler confirmed, finishing the equation on the board: x = 2.

The rest of the class was a whirlwind of equations and solutions, each one bringing them a step closer to the hidden treasure. With every equation they solved, Mr. Euler marked a spot on the map. The spots seemed random at first, but as more were added, they began to form a pattern. It was as if the algebra was slowly painting a path to the treasure.

By the end of the class, they had solved a series of equations, each more challenging than the last. However, the treasure's location was still a mystery. The path on the map was incomplete, but they had made significant progress.

As the bell rang, signaling the end of class, Mia, Leo, and Priya gathered their things slowly, their eyes lingering on the map. "Who would've thought algebra could lead to treasure?" Priya mused, her eyes sparkling with excitement.

Leo, always the logical one, pushed his glasses up the bridge of his nose. "It's not just about the treasure," he said. "It's about the journey—the puzzles we solve, the things we discover along the way."

Mia nodded in agreement, her mind already racing with the possibilities of their next class. "And the best part is," she added, "the adventure has just begun."
As they left the classroom, the map on Mr. Euler's desk seemed to shimmer under the fluorescent lights, as if keeping a secret. Algebra had become more than a subject—it was a key, a map, a puzzle, and an adventure all rolled into one. And they couldn't wait to see where it would lead them next.

CHAPTER 3 OVERVIEW

Concepts Covered

- **SOLVING EQUATIONS:** This chapter focused on the technique of solving basic algebraic equations. The solutions to these equations are the values that make the equation true.
- **ORDER OF OPERATIONS:** Understanding the order of operations, often remembered by the acronym PEMDAS (Parentheses, Exponents, Multiplication and Division, Addition and Subtraction), is crucial when solving equations.

Practical Applications

Solving equations and understanding the order of operations are fundamental skills in algebra. They allow us to solve a wide variety of problems in different fields such as physics, engineering, and economics.

Key Equations or Formulas

An example from this chapter is $5x - 3 = 7$. To solve this equation, we first add 3 to both sides to get $5x = 10$, then divide both sides by 5 to get $x = 2$.

Practice Problems

Problems
1. Solve the equation for x: $3x - 2 = 7$
2. Solve the equation for y: $2(y - 3) = 8$
3. Solve the equation for z: $z / 4 + 2 = 5$
4. Solve the equation for a: $3(2a - 1) = 9$

Solutions
1. Add 2 to both sides to get $3x = 9$, then divide both sides by 3 to get $x = 3$.
2. Using the order of operations, first distribute the 2 to get $2y - 6 = 8$, then add 6 to both sides to get $2y = 14$, and finally divide both sides by 2 to get $y = 7$.
3. Subtract 2 from both sides to get $z / 4 = 3$, then multiply both sides by 4 to get $z = 12$.
4. First distribute the 3 to get $6a - 3 = 9$, then add 3 to both sides to get $6a = 12$, and finally divide both sides by 6 to get $a = 2$.

CHAPTER 4

The Path of Variables

The following day, Room 314 was buzzing with whispers of the impending algebra class. News of the treasure map had spread throughout the school, and Mia, Leo, and Priya felt a sense of pride. They were at the heart of this algebraic adventure. As they walked into the classroom, they couldn't help but feel a rush of excitement.

Mr. Euler was already in the room, the treasure map spread out on his desk. Today, however, he seemed even more excited. "Good morning, adventurers!" he greeted, his eyes twinkling with anticipation. "Are we ready to uncover the next algebraic clue?"

The entire class responded with an enthusiastic 'yes', their eagerness palpable. Mr. Euler moved to the smartboard and wrote down the day's equation: $3x + 4 = 13$.

"Our goal remains the same: isolate 'x'." Mr. Euler began. "So, who can suggest our first step?"

Priya, who had been quietly studying the equation, finally

found her voice. "We should subtract 4 from both sides to eliminate the '+4' on the left side."

Mr. Euler beamed at her. "Excellent, Priya! Now, our equation looks like this: $3x = 9$."

Leo was quick to take the next step. "And if we divide both sides by 3, we get '$x = 3$'."

The class scribbled down the solution, but the trio couldn't help but look at the map. Mr. Euler didn't disappoint. He marked the third spot on the map, and for the first time, they saw a clear path forming. It led from the outskirts of a beautifully illustrated forest to the banks of a winding river.

"But that's not the end of our journey today," Mr. Euler announced, drawing their attention back to the board.

"We're going to explore something new—equations with variables on both sides."

He wrote down a new equation: $2x + 3 = x + 7$. The classroom went silent as they took in the complexity of the equation.

Mia, her mind already working through the problem, was the first to break the silence. "To start, we should make sure 'x' is only on one side. We could subtract 'x' from both sides to achieve that."

"Brilliant, Mia!" Mr. Euler praised, adjusting the equation to $2x - x + 3 = 7$, which simplified to $x + 3 = 7$.

Leo was quick to spot the next step. "Now it's like our earlier equations. We subtract 3 from both sides to isolate 'x', which gives us 'x = 4'."

Mr. Euler marked the fourth spot on the map, now near the top of a mountain. The class was thrilled; they were getting closer to the treasure. The room buzzed with speculation about what the treasure might be—a secret formula, a legendary mathematical artifact, or perhaps something beyond their wildest imaginations.

The bell rang, marking the end of another exciting class. As they packed their bags, Mia, Leo, and Priya couldn't help but marvel at the adventure they were on. They were not only learning algebra, but they were also living it. They were eager for the next class, ready to solve more equations and uncover more clues.

Algebra was no longer a subject they learned. It was a journey they embarked on, a mystery they were unraveling, and an adventure they were living. As they left Room 314, they knew they were one step closer to finding the hidden treasure. And they couldn't wait to uncover what lay ahead.

CHAPTER 4 OVERVIEW

Concepts Covered

- **COMBINING LIKE TERMS:** This chapter introduced the concept of combining like terms, which simplifies expressions and makes them easier to work with.
- **DISTRIBUTIVE PROPERTY:** The distributive property allows us to multiply a single term and two or more terms within parentheses. This is crucial for simplifying algebraic expressions.

Practical Applications

Combining like terms and understanding the distributive property is a key aspect of simplifying and solving algebraic equations. These concepts are used in a variety of real-world situations, such as simplifying calculations in business, science, and engineering.

Key Equations or Formulas

An example from this chapter is simplifying $2x + 3 = x + 7$. By combining like terms, we get $2x - x + 3 = 7$, which simplified to $x + 3 = 7$.

Practice Problems

Problems
1. Simplify the expression: $4x + 3y - 2x + y$
2. Simplify the expression: $5(x - 3) + 2$
3. Simplify the expression: $3(2y + 4) - y$
4. Simplify the expression: $7z - 2(3z - 4)$

Solutions
1. Combine like terms to get $2x + 4y$.
2. Using the distributive property, this simplifies to $5x - 15 + 2$, or $5x - 13$.
3. Using the distributive property and combining like terms, this simplifies to $6y + 12 - y$, or $5y + 12$.
4. Using the distributive property and combining like terms, this simplifies to $7z - 6z + 8$, or $z + 8$.

CHAPTER 5

The Equation of the Forest

Mia, Leo, and Priya, once ordinary students, now felt like adventurers. Each day brought a new algebraic riddle, a new clue on the treasure map, and a new sense of excitement. As they walked into Room 314 on the third day of their adventure, they couldn't help but glance at the treasure map. It was no longer just a piece of parchment; it was a gateway to a world of mystery and discovery.

Mr. Euler greeted them with his usual enthusiasm. He was more than a teacher now; he was their guide on this grand adventure. He walked over to the smartboard, ready to uncover the secrets hidden within the equation of the day.

The equation that appeared before them was a two-step equation: "$2x + 5 = 13$." Mia, Leo, and Priya's curiosity piqued as they pondered the steps required to unravel its solution.

Leo's hand shot up, excitement glimmering in his eyes. "To solve this two-step equation, we need to isolate the variable x. First, let's get rid of the 5 on the left side of the equation. Since 5 is being added, we can subtract 5 from both sides."

Mr. Euler nodded, impressed by Leo's understanding. "That's correct, Leo! By subtracting 5 from both sides, we eliminate the addition of 5 on the left side, resulting in $2x = 8$."

Mia chimed in, her voice filled with determination. "Now, we need to isolate x further. The variable x is being multiplied by 2. To undo this multiplication, we divide both sides of the equation by 2."

Priya eagerly completed the steps. "Dividing both sides by 2 gives us x = 4. We've solved the equation!"

The classroom erupted in applause as the students celebrated their success. But little did they know that their triumph had awakened the enchanted forest within the treasure map. Suddenly, a vibrant light burst forth from the map, engulfing the room in a magical glow.

As the light faded, Mr. Euler's eyes gleamed with excitement. "Your incredible mathematical skills have unlocked a new dimension in our adventure. Behold, the Equation of the Forest!"

The once static map now seemed alive, showcasing a dense forest teeming with mystical creatures and hidden trails. Amongst the towering trees, symbols of inequality gleamed, beckoning the trio forward.

"Inequalities," Mr. Euler declared with a sense of awe, "are equations that use inequality symbols instead of equals. They allow us to compare values and explore relationships in a dynamic way."

Leo's curiosity sparked. "Can you show us an example, Mr. Euler?"

"Certainly, Leo!" Mr. Euler replied. "Let's consider the inequality 3x + 2 < 10. Our task is to find the range of values that make this inequality true."

Mia leaned forward, eager to dive into the problem. "To solve this inequality, we follow a similar process as with equations. First, let's subtract 2 from both sides to isolate the term with x."

Leo's eyes lit up as he jumped in. "So, $3x + 2 - 2 < 10 - 2$ simplifies to $3x < 8$."

Priya joined in, her voice confident. "To find x, we divide both sides of the inequality by 3. So, $3x/3 < 8/3$."

Mia's mind worked quickly. "That gives us $x < 8/3$. But let's express it as a decimal. Dividing 8 by 3 gives approximately 2.67. So, our solution is $x < 2.67$."

Mr. Euler beamed with pride. "Excellent work, my intrepid adventurers! You've discovered the range of values that satisfy the inequality. By expressing the solution as $x < 2.67$, we understand that x can be any value less than 2.67."

Leo, Mia, and Priya exchanged triumphant smiles. They were starting to see the power of inequalities and how they allowed them to explore relationships and make comparisons. The enchanted forest seemed to come alive with anticipation as they embraced this newfound knowledge.

As the class continued, Mr. Euler presented more examples of inequalities, each one challenging the trio to think critically and apply their problem-solving skills. They encountered inequalities with greater than symbols

(>), less than symbols (<), as well as greater than or equal to symbols (≥) and less than or equal to symbols (≤). With each example, they became more adept at analyzing the relationships between quantities and interpreting the results.

The enchanted forest responded to their efforts, revealing hidden paths and enchanting creatures that seemed to cheer them on. Each solved inequality brought them closer to the heart of the forest and their next adventure.

CHAPTER 5 OVERVIEW

Concepts Covered

- **TWO-STEP EQUATIONS:** Two-step equations require two operations to solve.
- **INEQUALITIES:** The chapter introduced inequalities, which are equations that use inequality symbols instead of equals. The symbols include > (greater than), < (less than), ≥ (greater than or equal to), and ≤ (less than or equal to).

Practical Applications

Two-step equations and inequalities are fundamental in algebra and are used in a variety of real-world situations, such as determining the best solutions in business operations, comparing data in statistics, and even in coding algorithms.

Key Equations or Formulas

$3x + 2 < 10$

To solve an inequality, we perform similar operations as with equations to isolate the variable.

Subtracting 2 from both sides: $3x + 2 - 2 < 10 - 2$
Simplifying: $3x < 8$
Dividing both sides by 3: $3x/3 < 8/3$
Solution: $x < 2.67$ (or expressed as a decimal)

Practice Problems

Problems
1. Solve the two-step equation: $3x - 4 = 11$
2. Solve the inequality: $2y + 3 > 7$
3. Solve the two-step equation: $4z + 2 = 18$
4. Solve the inequality: $3a - 5 \leq 10$

Solutions
1. Add 4 to both sides to get $3x = 15$, then divide both sides by 3 to get $x = 5$.
2. Subtract 3 from both sides to get $2y > 4$, then divide both sides by 2 to get $y > 2$.
3. Solution: Subtract 2 from both sides to get $4z = 16$, then divide both sides by 4 to get $z = 4$.
4. Solution: Add 5 to both sides to get $3a \leq 15$, then divide both sides by 3 to get $a \leq 5$.

CHAPTER 6

The Mountain of Fractions

Room 314 echoed with anticipation as Mia, Leo, and Priya stepped before the grand "Mountain of Fractions" sketched on their classroom map. The chalky drawing loomed large, each tricky path representing a unique fraction operation.

Their teacher, Mr. Euler, gestured to the mountain with a chuckle, "Today, adventurers, we'll tackle fraction operations and master the art of decimal conversion."

The first path snaking up the mountain bore the name "Addition and Subtraction". Here, the challenge was straightforward: "½ + ¼ and ¾ - ½". Mia squinted at the problems, her fingers tracing the equations in the air. "Remember, we can only add or subtract fractions when the denominators are the same."

She turned to her friends, her eyes gleaming. "For the first problem, if we convert ½ to ²⁄₄, we can add it to ¼. That gives us ¾." She quickly moved on to the next problem, "Again, if we think of ¾ as ⁶⁄₈, then we can subtract ⁴⁄₈, which is equivalent to ½, from it, and we get ²⁄₈, which simplifies to ¼."

As they successfully navigated this first path, a new one appeared, marked "Multiplication and Division". The challenges posed were: "⅔ * ¾ and ¾ ÷ ½".

Leo, eyes focused on the equations, began to unravel the problems, "Multiplication is simpler with fractions. We just multiply the top numbers, or numerators, and the bottom numbers, or denominators. So, ⅔ * ¾ equals ⁶⁄₁₂. We can simplify that by dividing both the numerator and the denominator by 6 to get ½."

He took a deep breath before diving into the next problem, "Division is a bit different. We multiply the first fraction by the reciprocal, or upside-down version, of the second fraction. So, ¾ ÷ ½ is the same as ¾ * ²⁄₁. That gives us ⁶⁄₄, which we can simplify to 1.5 if we express it as a decimal."

Having mastered the operations, they reached a higher ledge named "Fraction to Decimal Conversion". The etched challenge on the ledge read: "Convert ⅖ to a decimal and express 0.75 as a fraction."

Priya, who had been quietly contemplating, now joined the conversation, "Decimals and fractions are just two ways of expressing the same thing. To convert ⅖ to a decimal, we can divide 2 by 5. If we do that, we get 0.4."

The trio then looked at the second part of the problem, and Mia chimed in, "For converting 0.75 to a fraction, we remember that the decimal place counts 'tenths'. So, 0.75 is the same as 75/100. Simplifying that fraction by dividing the numerator and the denominator by 25 gives us ¾."

As soon as Mia had finished solving the equation, they were transported to the peak of the mountain. The views over the landscape below were spectacular, and they were thrilled to be there. Mr. Euler handed them a small flag with the school's emblem on it, and they planted it on the summit just like explorers before them had done.

Having reached the peak of the mountain, they had a moment to catch their breaths and celebrate their newfound confidence in fraction operations and conversions. But it wasn't long until the next adventure was before them.

As they glanced back at their classroom map, a bright light shone and an old piece of paper flew around the room and then landed gently into Mia's hand.

"To find the treasure, follow the Path of Linear Functions", it said. So, their next adventure was already in sight, promising more thrilling mathematical discoveries. Excitement bubbled within them as they packed up their bags, ready to tackle the next day's journey.

CHAPTER 6 OVERVIEW

Concepts Covered

- **FRACTION OPERATIONS:** This chapter delved into fraction operations - addition, subtraction, multiplication, and division of fractions, which is fundamental in algebra.
- **FRACTION TO DECIMAL CONVERSION:** Understanding how to convert fractions to decimals and vice versa is a key concept in algebra and was covered in this chapter.

Practical Applications

Fraction operations and conversions are used in everyday life situations such as cooking, shopping, and budgeting. They're also essential in various fields like engineering, physics, and computer science.

Key Equations or Formulas

An example is adding the fractions $\frac{1}{4}$ and $\frac{2}{3}$. To do this, you need a common denominator. In this case, the least common denominator is 12, so you convert the fractions to $\frac{3}{12}$ and $\frac{8}{12}$, then add them to get $\frac{11}{12}$.

Sample Problems and Solutions

Problems

1. Add the fractions: $\frac{1}{3} + \frac{1}{2}$
2. Multiply the fractions: $\frac{2}{3} * \frac{3}{4}$
3. Convert the fraction $\frac{3}{4}$ to a decimal.
4. Divide the fractions: $\frac{3}{4} \div \frac{2}{3}$

Solutions

1. Convert to fractions with a common denominator (6) to get $\frac{2}{6} + \frac{3}{6}$, which simplifies to $\frac{5}{6}$.
2. Multiply the numerators to get 6 and the denominators to get 12, resulting in $\frac{6}{12}$ which simplifies to $\frac{1}{2}$.
3. Divide the numerator by the denominator to get 0.75.
4. Multiply the first fraction by the reciprocal of the second to get $\frac{3}{4} * \frac{3}{2}$, which simplifies to $\frac{9}{8}$ or $1\frac{1}{8}$.

CHAPTER 7

The Path of Linear Functions

The morning sun cast long shadows on the school's basketball court. Mia, Leo, and Priya stood huddled together, a sense of anticipation in the air. They had in their hands the mystery parchment from the Mountain of Fractions, and the words, "To find the treasure, follow the Path of Linear Functions," were the driving force behind their gathering.

The three friends spent a moment in silence, each lost in thought. Finally, Mia broke the silence, "I remember Mr. Euler teaching us about linear functions. They're about things that move in a straight line."

Leo, holding a basketball under his arm, had a spark of inspiration. He dribbled the ball across the court, observing its straight path. "Like this ball," he suggested. "When I pass it, it moves in a straight line."

"That's true!" Priya exclaimed. "And the ball's speed is like the constant rate of change in a linear function." She picked up a second basketball, bouncing it lightly.

43

"If I pass this ball to Mia at the same speed, the rate of change is constant. But if I pass it to her faster or slower, the rate of change varies."

This prompted a lively discussion between the friends, each contributing their understanding of linear functions. With a growing sense of purpose, they spent the day turning the basketball court into a playground of mathematics. They visualized the court as a large graph, with the basketball's movements representing the linear equations they had learned about.

After a while, they decided to take a break and sat under the comforting shade of a nearby tree. Each of them had a piece of paper and a pencil, ready to document their real-life equations. Mia initiated the conversation, "Remember Mr. Euler's lesson on slope-intercept form? The formula $y = mx + b$?"

Leo nodded, recalling the lesson. "'m' is the slope, which is the rate of change, and 'b' is the y-intercept, the starting point of the line on the y-axis."

"And the slope tells us how steep the line is," Priya added, sketching a couple of lines with different slopes. "If I pass the ball to Mia quickly, the 'slope' or steepness of the line is greater than if I pass it slowly."

They spent the next few hours reenacting their passes on the court and then drawing them on their makeshift coordinate planes. They measured the distance of each

pass (the 'y') and the time it took (the 'x'), then calculated the slope by dividing the change in y by the change in x. The starting point, where the ball began its journey, was the y-intercept, noted as 'b'.

As the sun began to lower in the sky, they reviewed the linear equations they had created, each one a snapshot of their passes on the court. Yet, despite their progress, the treasure remained elusive, and the clue still somewhat cryptic. Exhausted yet exhilarated, they decided to meet again the next day to continue their adventure.

Just as they were about to part ways, Mia's phone buzzed. She opened a new message from Mr. Euler that read, "The treasure lies where the lines meet." The trio was left staring at the screen in wonder.

"Lines...as in the paths of the basketball?" Leo asked, scratching his head.

"And 'where the lines meet'... could he be referring to the point of intersection?" Priya added, her eyes lighting up with excitement.

With new energy pulsing through them, they agreed to meet early the next day, eager to solve the mystery of the intersecting lines and find the hidden treasure. They parted with their heads buzzing with concepts of linear functions, slope-intercept form, slopes, y-intercepts, and intersecting lines. Their adventure was far from over, and the thrill of discovery promised more excitement for the days to come.

CHAPTER 7 OVERVIEW

Concepts Covered

- **LINEAR FUNCTIONS:** This chapter introduced the concept of linear functions, which are equations that graph as a straight line.
- **SLOPE-INTERCEPT FORM:** The chapter also covered the slope-intercept form of a linear equation, $y = mx + b$, where m represents the slope and b represents the y-intercept.

Practical Applications

Linear functions are used in various real-life situations, from calculating speed to predicting future growth in business.

Key Equations or Formulas

A core example from this chapter is the linear equation in slope-intercept form, represented by $y = mx + b$. In the context of our story, if we were to consider the path of the basketball as a linear function, we could represent it by an equation like $y = 2x + 3$.

In this equation, the slope of the line (m) is 2. This number represents the basketball's constant speed or rate of change - for each unit of time that passes, the basketball covers a distance of 2 units.

The y-intercept (b) is 3. This number is the starting point of the ball's path - when the time is zero ($x = 0$), the basketball is at position 3 on the court.

Practice Problems

1. If you throw a basketball with a constant speed, how would you represent this as a linear function? Draw a graph to illustrate this function.

2. If a basketball is passed with a speed of 3 meters per second, what is the slope of the line representing this situation? Draw a line on a graph to represent this situation.

3. If a basketball starts from 2 meters away and is thrown with a speed of 3 meters per second, what is the linear function representing this situation? Plot this function on a graph.

4. In a game, a player passes the ball with a speed of 4 meters per second from a distance of 1 meter. What is the y-intercept of the line representing this situation? Draw a graph of the function representing this situation.

Solutions

1. The linear function would be y = mx, where m is the constant speed of the basketball. In this case, y represents the distance the ball has traveled, and x is the time. On the graph, the line should go up in a straight line, showing that the distance the basketball travels increases consistently with time. The graph below shows m=5.

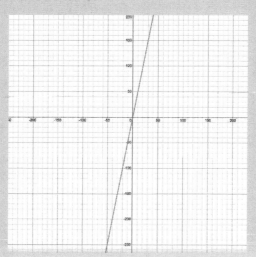

2. The slope is 3, as the ball moves 3 meters for every second. On the graph, the line should go up at a consistent angle, showing that for every second (x), the basketball travels three meters (y).

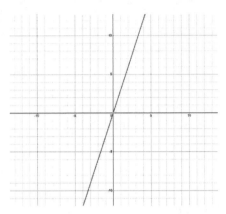

3. The linear function is y = 3x + 2, where 3 is the slope (speed) and 2 is the y-intercept (starting distance). The graph should start from the point (0,2) on the y-axis and rise consistently at an angle representing a speed of 3 meters per second.

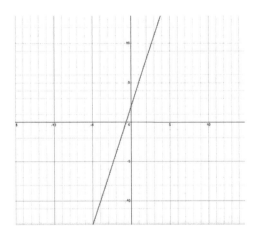

4. The y-intercept is 1, representing the starting distance of the pass. On the graph, the line should start at the point (0,1) and rise consistently at an angle representing a speed of 4 meters per second.

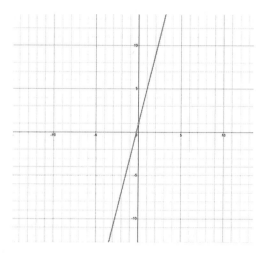

CHAPTER 8

The Intersection of Systems

As the sun cast long shadows on the school grounds, Mia, Priya, and Leo assembled, each energized for a new mathematical quest. Mia opened Mr. Euler's latest cryptic hint: "The treasure lies where the lines meet." The words echoed around them, generating a whirlwind of thoughts.

"Lines... like the ones we graphed yesterday?" Leo suggested, deep in thought.

"Exactly!" Priya's eyes sparkled with excitement. "And where lines intersect, they form a point. That means we're looking for a point of intersection."

A light bulb switched on in Mia's mind. "So we need a system of equations! A system is two or more equations with the same variables. The solutions are the points of intersection on the graph."

"Does that mean we have to find two equations and solve them simultaneously?" Leo asked, both his excitement and nervousness palpable.

"That's exactly what it means," Priya confirmed, her voice brimming with confidence.

The school then morphed into a maze of clues leading to these elusive equations. The friends became detectives, dissecting each clue to form an equation, bringing them tantalizingly closer to the treasure.

The mural on the school wall depicted a skateboarder ascending a ramp at a consistent angle. "That's like a line with a positive slope!" Mia exclaimed. "And look, the mural shows the skateboarder traveling 2 meters every second." She swiftly scribbled down the first equation: $y = 2x + 3$.

Meanwhile, Leo studied the floor's tile pattern. He noticed a consistent decrease, moving diagonally from one corner of the floor to another. "Each tile is one meter wide, and for every tile we move to the right, we move one down. That's a slope of -1. And we start 5 tiles up. So the second equation is $y = -x + 5$."

Armed with two equations, they eagerly plotted the lines on their graph paper. "Look! The lines intersect here," Mia declared, pointing at a spot on the graph. "If we're correct, the treasure should be at this intersection, which is (2, 1)."

"But how do we translate this into real-world coordinates?" Leo wondered.

"If we've been using the school as our coordinate plane, each unit on our graph can correspond to a meter on the school grounds," Priya proposed.

They started from the mural (0,0), took two steps to the right and one forward. To their delight, the intersection point led them to the old oak tree. Among its ancient roots, they found a small wooden box.

Inside the box was a note, which simply read, "Well done, but I believe you can achieve more. You must first substitute and eliminate and then you will find the treasure."

Energized by their victory, the trio didn't waste any time in diving into the next clue. "You must first substitute and eliminate...," Mia read aloud from the note, her voice filled with a mix of curiosity and excitement. But their joy was tempered by a note of confusion. "What does that mean?"

"I think..." Leo started, his eyes squinting at the mural on the school wall. "I think the mural and the tile pattern has given us two new equations. But this time, it's not as straightforward."

Priya followed Leo's gaze, taking in the intricate mural depicting the school's history and the mathematical symbols cleverly woven into the images. At the same time, she noticed the tiles on the floor forming patterns that seemed to hint at another equation.

Mia whipped out her notebook, ready to translate their observations into mathematical language. "Let's see. From the mural, the equation could be $y = 2x + 3$," she proposed, her brows furrowed in concentration. "And from the tiles... Maybe $y = -x + 2$?"

Leo nodded, "That sounds about right. Now, how do we solve this system of equations?"

The friends had already figured out one method -

graphing. But they knew that wasn't the only way to solve a system of linear equations. Priya recalled their math teacher, Mr. Euler, mentioning two other methods: substitution and elimination.

"Let's try substitution," suggested Priya. "It means we replace one variable in one equation with the same variable from the other equation."

Mia wrote the two equations next to each other in her notebook, then carefully replaced the 'y' in the first equation with '-x + 2' from the second. After simplifying, she found the solution: $x = -1$.

Substituting this value back into the first equation gave them $y = 1$. "So the intersection point is at (-1, 1)," Mia confirmed, her finger tracing the point on her sketch of the school grounds.

This time, interpreting the coordinates creatively, they used the oak tree as their starting point. Taking one step back (representing -1) and one to the right (representing 1), they uncovered another wooden box nestled among the roots. Inside was a mathematical treatise on exponents - an ancient-looking book filled with equations and diagrams, a true treasure for any math enthusiast.

"But wait," Leo mused, looking at the two equations in Mia's notebook. "Couldn't we have also used elimination to find the intersection point?"

"Absolutely," Mia confirmed, flipping to a new page in her notebook. "By adding the two equations together, we can eliminate one variable and solve for the other. Like this." She quickly demonstrated, and sure enough, the result was the same: the intersection point was (-1, 1).

This confirmation added a cherry on top of their mathematical victory. As they reveled in their success, a note fell out from the back of the book. It read, "Well done, you have found the treasure! These are mathematical tools of the past, and they will come in very handy on your journey. The secrets of exponents await you."

CHAPTER 8 OVERVIEW

Concepts Covered

- **SYSTEMS OF LINEAR EQUATIONS:** This chapter explored systems of linear equations, which involve two or more linear equations working together.
- **SOLVING SYSTEMS OF LINEAR EQUATIONS:** The chapter also covered methods for solving systems of linear equations, including graphing, substitution, and elimination.

Practical Applications

Systems of linear equations are used in various fields like business for profit and loss analysis, in physics for motion and force calculations, and in computer graphics for creating realistic visuals. Our adventurers had to solve a system of equations to find the intersection point that helped them move forward in their journey.

Key Equations or Formulas

Examples from this chapter are the systems of equations:

The first system:
y = 2x + 3
y = -x + 5
The intersection point of these two lines, which is (2,1), is the solution to this system.

The second system:
y = 2x + 3
y = -x + 2
The intersection point of these two lines, which is (-1,1), is the solution to this system.

Remember, these intersection points are where the 'lines meet,' as suggested by Mr. Euler's hint, and the points can be translated into physical locations based on the context provided in the problem.

Practice Problems

1. Solve the system of equations: y = 2x + 1 and y = -x + 3

2. Solve the system of equations: 2x + 3y = 12 and x - y = 2 by substitution.

3. Solve the system of equations: $3x + 2y = 11$ and $6x - y = 5$ by elimination.

4. Solve the system of equations: $y = 3x - 2$ and $y = -2x + 5$ graphically.

Solutions

1. Set the equations equal to each other: $2x + 1 = -x + 3$. Solving for x gives $x = 2/3$. Substituting $x = 2/3$ into the first equation gives $y = 2*(2/3) + 1 = 5/3$.
2. From the second equation, $x = y + 2$. Substitute this into the first equation: $2(y + 2) + 3y = 12$. Solving for y gives $y = 2$, and substituting $y = 2$ into the second equation gives $x = 4$.
3. Multiply the first equation by 2 and the second by 1 to align the coefficients of x. Then subtract the second equation from the first: $5y = 17$. Solving for y gives $y = 17/5 = 3.4$. Substituting $y = 3.4$ into the first equation gives $x = 4.2/3 = 1.4$.
4. Graphing these equations shows they intersect at the point (1, 1).

CHAPTER 9

The Power of Exponents

The morning sun spilled over the quiet school as the three friends gathered again, their minds still buzzing from the previous day's discovery. The antique mathematical instruments they had found were splayed out on the table, the gleaming metal and polished wood a tangible testament to their recent victory. The accompanying note, with its cryptic message, was spread out next to them, the words "The secrets of the exponents await you" seeming to shimmer with promise and challenge.

"Exponents," Leo began, his eyes reflecting the curiosity that sparked within him. He picked up the slide rule, an instrument used for complex mathematical calculations before the advent of the digital calculator. Turning it over in his hands, he traced the engraved lines and numbers with his finger. "These are used for multiplication and division, right? And exponents, they're a way of showing repeated multiplication, like 2^3 is 2 multiplied by itself 3 times, which equals 8, correct?"

"Exactly," Priya confirmed, her eyes brightening. "Exponents are a shorthand for repeated multiplication, and they're used to represent really big numbers or really small fractions. Think about it, writing 2^{10} is much easier than writing 2 multiplied by itself ten times."

Mia, always the one to dive deeper, began outlining the rules of exponents. "Remember, exponents follow specific rules that make calculations easier. For instance, the power of a power rule means that when you raise a power to another power, you multiply the exponents, like $(2^3)^2$ equals 2^6. The product of powers rule means that when you multiply numbers with the same base, you add the exponents, like 2^3 times 2^2 equals 2^5. The quotient of powers rule means that when you divide numbers with the same base, you subtract the exponents, like 2^5 divided by 2^3 equals 2^2. And the zero exponent rule tells us that any non-zero number raised to the power of zero equals one."

Mr. Euler, who had joined them, nodded approvingly. "Very good, Mia. Understanding these laws will be vital to your next adventure. The use of these rules can simplify the work with exponents and make the complex calculations easier."

"And you're doing so well, that I think I can step it up a bit," Mr. Euler continued, "so I'm going to introduce two other important aspects of exponents, namely negative and fractional exponents. When an exponent is negative, like 2^{-3}, it's the same as 1 divided by the positive

exponent, or 1/(2^3). That's the negative exponent rule. As for fractional exponents, they correspond to roots. For example, 2^(½) is the same as the square root of 2. Understanding these rules will make you experts at exponents."

The friends immersed themselves in the world of exponents over the next few days. They worked on multiplication and division of powers, raising a power to another power, understanding zero, negative, and fractional exponents. They also explored the slide rule, using it to perform multiplication, division, and even root and exponential calculations, which deepened their understanding of logarithms – the inverse of exponential functions.

During this period of intense study, a clue from the Keeper of the Algebraic Secrets appeared in front of them. A riddle disguised as a simple story problem: "A population starts at 100 and doubles every day. After how many days will it exceed a million?"

Recognizing this as an exponential growth problem, they knew they could solve it by setting up an exponential equation and then applying the laws of exponents. Working together, they formulated the equation: $100 * 2^d > 1,000,000$, where d represented the number of days. After some careful calculations, they found the answer.

"It takes 14 days," Mia announced. "After 14 days, the population will exceed a million."

And so, they continued, one riddle after another, each one pushing them deeper into the world of exponents. By the time they received the next clue, a note hinting at the location of the next treasure, they had become experts at manipulating and solving exponential equations, uncovering the pattern of exponential growth and decay, and realizing the prevalence of these patterns in the world around them.

The note read: "The treasure awaits at the base of the tallest power." Understanding that "the tallest power" referred to the tallest building in the town, the old clock tower, and "the base" hinted at its bottom, they rushed to the clock tower.

There, hidden in the undergrowth, they found a small box. Inside it was a modern scientific calculator and a note that read, "Congratulations, you've mastered the power of exponents. But your adventure is far from over. The secrets of polynomials and factoring await you."

As they held their new treasure, the friends felt a surge of excitement for the journey ahead. They had unlocked the secrets of exponents, and were now ready to face the challenge of understanding polynomials and factoring. They were stepping into a world of mathematical expressions even more complex and intriguing, armed with their newfound knowledge and the tools of the past and present.

CHAPTER 9 OVERVIEW

Concepts Covered

- **EXPONENTS:** This chapter introduced the concept of exponents, which is a shorthand way to describe repeated multiplication of the same number.
- **RULES OF EXPONENTS:** The chapter also covered the basic rules of exponents, such as product rule, power rule, quotient rule, and the zero exponent rule.

Product Rule: When you multiply numbers with the same base, you add the exponents.

Power Rule: When you raise a power to another power, you multiply the exponents.

Quotient Rule: When you divide numbers with the same base, you subtract the exponents.

Zero Exponent Rule: Any non-zero number raised to the power of zero equals one.

Negative Exponent Rule: When an exponent is negative, it's equivalent to 1 divided by the base raised to the absolute value of the exponent.

Fractional Exponent Rule: Fractional exponents correspond to roots, such as a fractional exponent of ½ being equivalent to taking the square root of the base.

Practical Applications

Exponents are used in various real-life situations, such as calculating the growth of populations, understanding the size of microscopic elements, or determining the speed of computers. Our adventurers encountered a situation where understanding and applying the power of exponents helped them solve a crucial problem.

Key Equations or Formulas

The key equation in this chapter is related to the exponential growth problem that the friends solved. The equation they used was:

$100 * 2^d > 1,000,000$

In this equation, 100 represents the initial population, 2 is the growth factor (since the population doubles each day), d is the number of days, and 1,000,000 is the population size they wanted to exceed.

By solving this equation, they discovered that after 14 days, the population would exceed a million. This equation is an example of an exponential function.

Practice Problems

1. Cell Division: A type of bacteria divides every 20 minutes, starting with one bacterium. Using the formula for exponential growth, calculate how many bacteria will be present after 2 hours.

2. Investment Growth: You invest $500 in a bank account that has an annual interest rate of 5%, compounded annually. Write the exponential function that represents the amount of money in the account after 'n' years. Then, use this function to calculate how much money will be in the account after 10 years.

3. Computer Processing Power: The processing power of computers has historically doubled approximately every two years, a trend known as Moore's Law. If a computer has a processing power of 2 gigaflops (billion floating-point operations per second) today, write an exponential function to represent the computer's processing power 'p' after 't' years. Then, use this function to predict the computer's processing power in 5 years.

4. Radioactive Decay: A certain radioactive substance decays exponentially. It initially has a mass of 100 grams, and it loses 5% of its mass every day. Write an exponential function that represents the mass 'm' of the substance after 'd' days. Then, use this function to determine the mass of the substance after 7 days.

Solutions

1. Cell Division: The bacteria divide every 20 minutes, which means they divide 3 times in an hour. Therefore, in 2 hours, they divide 2*3 = 6 times. If we start with 1 bacterium, after 6 divisions we will have 2^6 = 64 bacteria.

2. Investment Growth: The exponential function that represents the amount of money in the account after 'n' years is A = 500*(1.05)^n. After 10 years, the amount of money in the account will be A = 500*(1.05)^10 ≈ $814.45.

3. Computer Processing Power: The exponential function that represents the computer's processing power 'p' after 't' years is p = 2*(2)^(t/2). After 5 years, the processing power will be:
   p = 2*(2)^($\frac{5}{2}$) ≈ 11.3 gigaflops.

4. Radioactive Decay: The exponential function that represents the mass 'm' of the substance after 'd' days is m = 100*(0.95)^d. After 7 days, the mass of the substance will be m = 100*(0.95)^7 ≈ 69.8 grams.

CHAPTER 10

Journey to Polynomial Palace

As the friends huddled around their new scientific calculator, a sudden transformation occurred. The display's numbers swirled into a vortex, and with a flash of light, they found themselves transported to a different realm – the Polynomial Palace.

Mr. Euler, who seemed unfazed by the sudden change in surroundings, was now donning royal robes. "Welcome, young mathematicians, to the Polynomial Palace," he declared, gesturing grandly towards the magnificent mathematical wonder around them. This was a realm where numbers towered like skyscrapers, and equations replaced brick and mortar.

Intrigued, Leo walked up to a wall constructed from blocks inscribed with expressions like "$3x^2 + 2x - 1$", "$4y^3 - 7y + 2$" and "$z^4 + z^3 - z - 1$". "These are all polynomials, right?" he asked, looking over at Mr. Euler for confirmation.

"Excellent observation, Leo," Mr. Euler acknowledged. "Polynomials are indeed algebraic expressions made up of one or more terms. The power, or exponent, of each term's variable must be a non-negative integer. That's the rule here in Polynomial Palace."

"But why do we need to know about polynomials?" asked Mia.

"Polynomials are not just intriguing mathematical concepts confined within the walls of this palace or your textbooks," Mr. Euler explained. "They have significant applications in the world outside. When engineers design bridges or architects plan buildings, they use polynomials to model structures and calculate stress distribution. In physics, they describe certain types of motion. Even in economics, polynomials help to model and analyze trends."

The friends looked at each other in amazement. It was thrilling to realize that the mathematical expressions they were learning about were so deeply embedded in everyday life. Their journey was not just about finding the treasure but also about appreciating the relevance and utility of mathematics in understanding and shaping the world around them.

"Ok, I'm ready to learn more!" said Mia, who had always dreamed of becoming an architect.

"Great, then let's get started." said Mr Euler, leading them ahead.

Their grand tour of the palace started with the Addition and Subtraction Room, a grand hall where numerical blocks seemed to dance in mid-air. Mr. Euler set them a challenge to solve puzzles by rearranging these floating blocks, with the rule that they could only move blocks with the same variable and exponent. This was a hands-on way to illustrate the principle of combining like terms.

"Remember, we can only add or subtract like terms – that is, terms with the same variable and exponent," Mr. Euler reminded them. They saw an equation floating above: "$3x^2 + 5x^2 - x$".

Leo thought aloud, "So, we can combine $3x^2$ and $5x^2$ because they are like terms. This gives us $8x^2$. And we can't combine the $-x$ because it's not a like term with x^2." The equation simplified to "$8x^2 - x$".

Soon enough, the friends had become proficient in adding and subtracting polynomials. Encouraged by their success, the trio moved onto the Multiplication Room, a different world with its own set of challenges. Here, they learned to multiply polynomials by stacking the blocks. Mr. Euler guided them through the process, helping them visualize the distributive property, which is essential when multiplying polynomials. Mr. Euler presented them an equation: "$(x + 2) * (x - 3)$".

Mia studied the equation and started to multiply each term of the first polynomial with each term of the second, a process known as distribution. She muttered, "So, we multiply x by each term of the second polynomial, and then 2 by each term of the second polynomial...". The equation became "$x^2 - 3x + 2x - 6$".

"Now simplify it by combining like terms," Mr. Euler prompted. Mia responded, "$-3x$ and $2x$ are like terms. So it simplifies to $x^2 - x - 6$."

The final challenge, the Factoring Room, lay in the palace's highest tower. Here, Mr. Euler introduced them to the reverse process of multiplication, factoring. The friends realized that factoring was like deconstructing the polynomial structures into simpler blocks – their factors.

On the wall was the equation "$x^2 - 5x + 6$". After staring at it for a moment, Leo noted, "Factoring is the reverse process of multiplying, so we have to think of two numbers that multiply to 6 and add to -5... ah, -2 and -3!" The equation factored into "$(x - 2) * (x - 3)$".

After days of exploration and learning, they reached the top of the palace, where a golden polynomial, "$3x^2 - x - 2$", awaited them. After a moment's pause, Mia began factoring it into "$(3x - 1) * (x + 2)$" - the key to the grand treasure chest that lay before them.

Inside the chest, they found a book brimming with more advanced mathematical knowledge, including quadratic equations–a topic they had heard a lot about but hadn't delved into yet. So holding the book tightly, they found themselves whisked back to their school, ready to unlock the mysteries of quadratic equations.

CHAPTER 10 OVERVIEW

Concepts Covered

*   **POLYNOMIALS:** This chapter introduced polynomials, which are expressions made up of coefficients and variables that are combined using addition, subtraction, and multiplication.
*   **DEGREES AND TERMS OF POLYNOMIALS:** The chapter also covered the structure of polynomials, including terms, coefficients, and degrees.
*   **ADDING AND SUBTRACTING POLYNOMIALS:** The adventurers learned how to add and subtract polynomials by combining like terms.

Practical Applications

Polynomials are widely used in numerous fields such as physics, engineering, and economics. They can model various phenomena like the trajectory of a ball, the design of roller coasters, or predicting economic growth.

Key Equations or Formulas

An example from this chapter is the polynomial $3x^2 + 2x - 1$. It's a second degree polynomial with three terms.

Practice Problems

1. Puzzle Quest: Imagine that you are in the Polynomial Palace, and you find a hidden door. To open it, you must add the following polynomials: $3x^2 - 4x + 1$ and $5x^2 + 2x - 3$. What polynomial do you get?

2. Block Multiplication: In the Multiplication room, you encounter a challenge where you must multiply $(2x - 5)$ with $(3x + 4)$. What is the resulting polynomial?

3. Factoring Fun: You find a golden block inscribed with the polynomial $x^2 - 6x + 9$. What are its factors?

4. <u>Real World Challenge:</u> Your friend is planning to sell handmade bracelets and wants to model her potential earnings. She plans to sell each bracelet for $15 and expects to sell 5 more each week. If we let x represent the number of weeks, and P(x) her potential earnings, write a polynomial to represent her earnings over time.

Solutions

1. <u>Puzzle Quest:</u> To add the polynomials $3x^2 - 4x + 1$ and $5x^2 + 2x - 3$, we combine like terms. The resulting polynomial is:

$$(3x^2 + 5x^2) + (-4x + 2x) + (1 - 3) = 8x^2 - 2x - 2.$$

2. <u>Block Multiplication:</u> To multiply $(2x - 5)$ with $(3x + 4)$, we use the distributive property:

$$(2x - 5) * (3x + 4) = 2x * 3x + 2x * 4 + (-5) * 3x + (-5) * 4$$
$$= 6x^2 + 8x - 15x - 20$$
$$= 6x^2 - 7x - 20.$$

3. <u>Factoring Fun:</u> The polynomial $x^2 - 6x + 9$ can be factored as follows:

$$x^2 - 6x + 9 = (x - 3)(x - 3) = (x - 3)^2.$$

4. <u>Real World Challenge:</u> Let's represent the number of weeks as x. The earnings for each week can be expressed as the product of the number of bracelets sold and the price per bracelet. The number of bracelets sold per week is given by x + 5 (starting with an initial sale of 5 bracelets). Therefore, the polynomial representing her earnings over time is:

$P(x) = (x + 5) * 15 = 15x + 75.$

CHAPTER 11

The Quadratic Quest

The friends were back in school, their minds still reeling from the adventure they had just experienced in the Polynomial Palace. They had unlocked the mysteries of polynomials and factoring, and they were ready for more adventures. The book they had discovered in the grand treasure chest was now guiding them towards a new challenge: quadratic equations.

Before they could delve into the book, the scientific calculator sprang to life. Its screen flickered, and a holographic figure of Mr. Euler emerged from it, now appearing as a regal guide in the land of mathematics.

"Bravo on your success in the Polynomial Palace," he commended, "Your next challenge delves into the realm of Quadratic Equations, second-degree polynomials that take the form $ax^2 + bx + c = 0$."

Leo, the most vocal of the group, quickly interjected, "Those are the ones that give a graph shaped like a parabola when plotted, right?"

"Absolutely correct, Leo," Mr. Euler affirmed. "The solutions to these equations, also known as the roots, are the x-coordinates where the parabola intersects the x-axis. Your task is to find these roots."

Just as Mr Euler had finished speaking, the old school library morphed into a mystical labyrinth filled with secret doors and hidden rooms. Each room was locked by an enchanted door, inscribed with a quadratic equation, waiting to be unlocked by the correct roots.

As the friends plunged deeper into the labyrinth, they realized that these weren't just ordinary doors. The keys to these doors were the solutions to the quadratic equations, and to find them, they had to master the quadratic formula.

With a determined look in their eyes, they approached the first door. Etched on its oak surface was the equation $3x^2 - 2x - 1 = 0$. They exchanged bewildered glances; how were they supposed to unlock a door with an equation?

Suddenly, the calculator crackled to life, and the glowing figure of Mr. Euler reappeared. "To navigate this labyrinth, you must understand the heart of quadratic equations — the quadratic formula," he said, his voice resonating in

the mystical surroundings. "Do you remember how to do it?"

Priya squinted at the door and then back at the calculator.

"Yes," she said, "it's x equals negative b plus or minus the square root of b squared minus 4ac, all divided by 2a. But, how do we apply that here?"

"Well," Mr. Euler explained, "in the equation $3x^2 - 2x - 1 = 0$, 'a' is 3, 'b' is -2, and 'c' is -1. Use the quadratic formula to find the roots, or 'x', of this equation. These roots will unlock the door."

With newfound understanding, the friends huddled together, applying the formula to the equation. There was a moment of silence as they computed the values. Mia, finally breaking the silence, exclaimed, "The roots are $x = 1$ and $x = -1/3$."

"Brilliant!" Mr. Euler commended. "Now, try using these roots as keys to the door."

As they announced the roots, a soft click echoed through the room. The grand door creaked open, revealing another passage, another door, another equation. The friends grinned at each other; they were one step closer to conquering the quadratic maze. The real adventure had just begun.

With their spirits invigorated, the friends stepped through the opened door, ready for the next challenge. In the new chamber, the air hummed with a strange energy, and in the center, they found a scale with an equation engraved on its base: $4x^2 - 4x - 3 = 0$.

"We need to find the roots for this equation, the balance points, to stabilize the scale," Leo reasoned, studying the peculiar instrument.

"Right," Priya chimed in. "Let's apply the quadratic formula again." They went through the steps together:

"a is 4, b is -4, and c is -3. So, according to the quadratic formula, x equals negative b plus or minus the square root of b squared minus 4ac, all divided by 2a."

Priya calculated it out loud: "So we get x equals 4 plus or minus the square root of $(-4)^2$ minus 44(-3), all divided by 2*4... which simplifies to 4 plus or minus the square root of 16 + 48, all divided by 8... further simplifying, we get 4 plus or minus the square root of 64, all divided by 8, which gives us 4 plus or minus 8 divided by 8."

Leo then exclaimed, "We've got x = -1/2 and x = 3/2!"

As they voiced the roots, the scale, which was precariously tilting, balanced perfectly. The once humming air became calm and, from the base of the scale, a path of glowing tiles lead them to the next door.

This pattern repeated as they ventured deeper into the labyrinth. With each challenge, they honed their skills, their understanding of quadratic equations deepening with every door they opened. It was not just about memorizing the quadratic formula, but also about understanding its application, the steps, and how the values of 'a', 'b', and 'c' influenced the roots.

The final door, a towering construction of iron and oak, presented the ultimate challenge. Its equation read $2x^2 - 6x - 8 = 0$. This was their chance to demonstrate everything they had learned. By now, they moved confidently, no longer daunted by the complex equations.

"Let's solve this, just like we did before," Mia suggested. After a moment of concentration, Priya started calculating:

"a is 2, b is -6, and c is -8. So according to the quadratic formula, x equals negative b plus or minus the square root of b squared minus 4ac, all divided by 2a."

She continued: "That gives us x equals 6 plus or minus the square root of $(-6)^2$ minus 42(-8), all divided by 2*2... simplifying, we get 6 plus or minus the square root of 36 + 64, all divided by 4... and that simplifies to 6 plus or minus the square root of 100, all divided by 4... which gives us 6 plus or minus 10 divided by 4."

Smiling broadly, Priya announced, "The roots are x = 4 and x = -1."

The door swung open, revealing a glowing chest. It opened to their touch, and inside lay another note. Mia read aloud, "Your next journey awaits you in the land of Functions and Graphs. Good luck, adventurers."

They looked at each other, grinning. Their success in this Quadratic Quest, the adrenaline of adventure mixed with the joy of understanding, had them thrilled for the next chapter of their mathematical journey.

CHAPTER 11 OVERVIEW

Concepts Covered

- **QUADRATIC EQUATIONS:** This chapter introduced quadratic equations, which are polynomial equations of the second degree.
- **STANDARD FORM OF A QUADRATIC EQUATION:** The chapter covered the standard form of a quadratic equation, $ax^2 + bx + c = 0$, where a, b, and c are constants.
- **SOLVING QUADRATIC EQUATIONS:** The adventurers learned about the methods to solve quadratic equations, such as factoring, completing the square, and the quadratic formula.

Practical Applications

Quadratic equations can model a wide range of scenarios in the physical world, such as the motion of objects under gravity, the shape of satellite dishes, or predicting the maximum profit in business. Our adventurers used their understanding of quadratic equations to complete their quest.

Key Equations or Formulas

The key equation in this chapter is the quadratic equation in the standard form:

$ax^2 + bx + c = 0$

And the formula to find the roots of this equation, known as the quadratic formula:

$x = [-b \pm sqrt(b^2 - 4ac)] / 2a$

Practice Problems

1. A stone is thrown upward from a bridge into a river below. Its height in meters above the water t seconds after being thrown is modeled by the equation $h(t) = -5t^2 + 20t + 15$. How long after the stone is thrown does it hit the water?

2. The area of a rectangular garden is given by the quadratic equation $x^2 - 5x - 24 = 0$, where x represents the length of the garden in meters. What are the possible lengths of the garden?

3. A basketball player shoots a ball towards the hoop. The path of the ball is modeled by the equation y = -0.5x^2 + 2x + 1, where y represents the height of the ball in meters and x represents the distance from the hoop in meters. At what distance from the hoop does the ball reach its maximum height?

4. A concert is selling tickets at $50 each. They calculate that for each $5 increase in ticket price, they'll have 10 fewer attendees. If the concert venue can hold 500 people maximum, what should the ticket price be to maximize revenue? The relationship can be modeled by a quadratic equation R(p) = -(p-50)^2 + 500, where R is the revenue and p is the price increase.

Solutions

1. For the stone's height, you set the equation equal to zero and use the quadratic formula to solve for the time t. The stone hits the water when h(t) = 0, so you solve the equation -5t^2 + 20t + 15 = 0. Using the quadratic formula, you get t = 1s or t = 3s. Since the stone can't hit the water before it is thrown, the answer is t = 3 seconds.

2. For the garden's length, you again set the equation equal to zero and solve for x using the quadratic formula. The possible lengths of the garden are the roots of the equation $x^2 - 5x - 24 = 0$. Using the quadratic formula, the solutions are x = 8 and x = -3. Since a garden can't have a negative length, the possible length of the garden is 8 meters.

3. For the basketball's path, you want to find the maximum height, which occurs at the vertex of the parabola. The ball reaches its maximum height at the vertex of the parabola, which is at x = -b/(2a) = -2/(2*-0.5) = 2 meters from the hoop.

4. For the concert's revenue, you also want to find the maximum, which again occurs at the vertex of the parabola. The maximum revenue is achieved at the vertex of the parabola, which is at p = -b/(2a) = -(-50)/(2*-1) = 25. So, the ticket price should be $50 (initial price) + $25 (increase) = $75 to maximize revenue.

CHAPTER 12

The Fascinating World of Functions and Graphs

It was an ordinary day at school when the friends met up for their study session. They were no longer just school mates - they were adventurers, explorers of the mathematical realms. Armed with their trusty scientific calculator and the magical book, they were eager to plunge into their next mathematical odyssey: Functions and Graphs.

As Leo opened the book, the scientific calculator sprang to life, projecting a holographic image of Mr. Euler. He was their guide in this mystical mathematical world. "Welcome back, explorers. Your journey will now take you into the intriguing world of Functions and Graphs."

"Mr. Euler, what are functions?" asked Mia, always ready with a question. With a kind smile, Mr. Euler began to explain. "Think of a function as a magical box. You input a number, and the box transforms it into a new number. It is a special kind of relation where each input, or 'x', gives you exactly one output, or 'y'."

Intrigued, the friends spent the next several days diving deep into the concept of functions. They learned to represent functions like $f(x) = 2x + 1$, where 'f(x)' was the output when a number 'x' was plugged into the function.

"But how do we see what these functions look like? It's all so abstract!" Leo puzzled one day.

"That's where graphing comes in," said Mr. Euler. "Just like a map represents a city, a graph represents a function. By plotting the function on a graph, we can see its shape and understand how 'y' changes with 'x'."

Armed with this knowledge, they set out on their first graphing quest. The chosen function was simple: $f(x) = x^2$. They plugged in different 'x' values into the function and got the corresponding

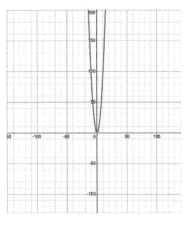

'y' values. Plotting these points on a graph, they connected the dots to reveal a curve that looked like a U – a parabola. It was a eureka moment as the numbers on the page came alive, forming a visual shape.

The friends started seeing functions and graphs everywhere around them. From the arc of a thrown football to the growth of plants, they began to understand how mathematical functions modeled the world. As they ventured deeper into different types of functions – linear, quadratic, exponential – they realized the power these mathematical tools held.

One day, as they sat together on their school's sports field, watching a football game, Leo suddenly exclaimed, "Hey, look at that! That's a parabola!" He was pointing at a football thrown in a high, arching trajectory.

Mia looked puzzled. "What do you mean? It's a football!" Leo, with a knowing smile, replied, "No, Mia, look at the path the football takes. It's shaped like a 'U', like the graph we drew for the function $f(x) = x^2$."

Suddenly, they all saw it. The high arc of the football, the way it rose and then descended, was indeed shaped like a parabola. The path of the football was a real-life illustration of the functions and graphs they had been studying.

With Mr. Euler's guidance, they modeled the football's trajectory as a quadratic function. First, they measured the time the football took to reach its highest point and then to hit the ground. This data helped them write a function representing the football's height at any given time.

After several attempts, they came up with a quadratic function: f(t) = -5t^2 + 20t, where 't' was the time since the football was thrown, and 'f(t)' was the height of the football.

To see this function visually, they decided to plot its graph.

They created a table of values, plugging in different times into the function to get corresponding heights. Then, they plotted these points on a graph. The resulting curve was a perfect parabola, opening downwards – a mirror image of the ones they had seen earlier because the coefficient of 't^2' was negative.

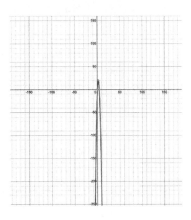

Examining the graph, Priya asked, "Can we find out when the ball hits the ground using this graph?"

Mr. Euler responded, "Indeed, we can! The point where the ball hits the ground is when its height, or 'f(t)', is zero. So, we need to find the root of the equation -5t^2 + 20t = 0."

Applying the quadratic formula, they found the roots to be t = 0 and t = 4. This indicated that the ball was on the ground at the start, which was at t = 0, and then again after 4 seconds, which was t = 4.

This hands-on exploration gave the friends a deeper understanding of functions and graphs. Not only were they able to model the real-world scenario with a function and graph it, but they also used the graph to make predictions.

The following day, they stumbled upon a mysterious door locked by a function: $f(x) = (x - 3)^2 - 4$. It was their biggest challenge yet. This was not just about solving an equation; it was about understanding the function's behavior through its graph.

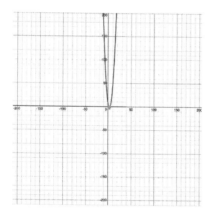

They drew up a table of values, plotting the points, and finally sketching the parabola. It shifted from the earlier one, reflecting the changes in coefficients and the constant.

With the graph drawn, it was time to solve the function. Applying their understanding of transformations of functions, they found that the roots were $x = 1$ and $x = 5$. They excitedly shouted out the solutions, and as they did, the graph in their hands shimmered and transformed into two keys, marked '1' and '5'. They inserted the keys into the door, and with a satisfying click, it swung open, revealing a new path.

Suddenly, a scroll appeared in front of them. It read: "By mastering Functions and Graphs, you have unlocked the path to your next adventure: Linear Equations."

CHAPTER 12 OVERVIEW

Concepts Covered

- **FUNCTIONS:** This chapter introduced functions, which are rules that relate inputs to outputs in a consistent way.
- **GRAPHS OF FUNCTIONS:** The chapter also covered how to graph functions, including linear, quadratic, and other types of functions.
- **INTERPRETING GRAPHS:** The adventurers learned to interpret and understand the real-world meanings of function graphs.

Practical Applications

Functions and their graphs are used in various real-world scenarios like predicting population growth, understanding the spread of a disease, or determining the optimal pricing for a product.

Key Equations or Formulas

The key equations in this chapter are the quadratic functions used to model the trajectory of the football and to unlock the door:

$$f(t) = -5t^2 + 20t$$

Here, 't' is the time since the football was thrown, and 'f(t)' is the height of the football. This equation helps to determine the height of the football at any given time, representing the path of the football as a parabola on a graph.

$$f(x) = (x - 3)^2 - 4$$

This quadratic function represents a parabola that has been shifted 3 units to the right and 4 units down from the standard position. The roots of this function, $x = 1$ and $x = 5$, were used to unlock the door.

Practice Problems

1. If Mia's dog, Rover, chases a ball that Mia throws for him, can you model Rover's path with a function? Assume Rover runs in a straight line at a constant speed.

2. You are planning a road trip. Your car can travel 25 miles per gallon of gas, and you have a budget of $100 for gas. If gas costs $2.50 per gallon, how far can you travel? Model this situation as a function and draw its graph.

3. Leo sells cookies at a school fair. He notices that if he prices his cookies at $2 each, he sells 50 cookies. For each 20 cent increase in price, he sells 5 fewer cookies. Can you model Leo's revenue as a function of the price of his cookies? What price will maximize Leo's revenue?

4. Priya is saving money for a new bicycle. She saves $10 per week from her allowance. If the bicycle costs $150, how many weeks does she need to save? Model Priya's savings as a function of time, and graph this function.

Solutions

1. Yes, Rover's path can be modeled as a linear function. Since Rover runs in a straight line at a constant speed, the function would be f(t) = vt. The graph of his path would be a straight line.

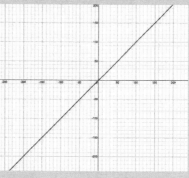

2. The function that models this situation is
   f(x) = 25x, where x is the number of gallons of gas.
   The budget constraint is $100 = $2.50 * x, solving
   for x gives x = 40. Substituting x = 40 into the
   function f(x) gives f(40) = 25 * 40 = 1000. So you
   can travel 1000 miles.

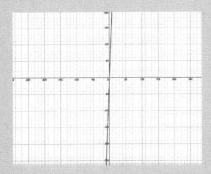

3. For Leo's problem, we're finding the price that
   maximizes his revenue from selling cookies.
   Revenue is price times quantity sold. We know as
   price increases by $0.20, quantity sold decreases
   by 5 cookies. We represent this relationship with
   a function. Solving for the price that maximizes
   revenue involves calculus, which is complex. So,
   without precise calculations, we can estimate that
   the optimal price will be a bit over $2, given that
   Leo starts selling cookies at $2 and sales decrease
   as the price increases.

4. The function that models this situation is f(t) =
   10t, where t is the number of weeks. To find out

how many weeks Priya needs to save, we set the function equal to $150 and solve for t. So, 150 = 10t, which gives t = 15. Priya needs to save for 15 weeks. The graph of the function is a straight line with a slope of 10 and y-intercept at 0.

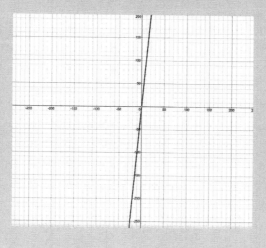

CHAPTER 13

The Enigma of Linear Equations

Once again, the group of friends found themselves in a strange new world as soon as they finished reading the scroll. The classroom they were in vanished, replaced by a bustling medieval marketplace. The air was filled with the chatter of vendors hawking their goods, the smell of fresh produce, and the clatter of horse-drawn carts.

The familiar voice of Mr. Euler came from their magical scientific calculator, "Welcome to Linear City, the hub of Linear Equations!"

Priya, slightly bewildered by the sudden shift, asked Mr. Euler, "What are linear equations? How are they different from the equations we've learned so far?"

Mr. Euler's holographic image smiled. "Priya, a linear equation is an equation that, when graphed, forms a straight line. They often take the form $y = mx + b$, where 'm' represents the slope of the line, and 'b' is the y-intercept, showing where the line crosses the y-axis."

Over the next few days, the friends immersed themselves in Linear City's unique culture, learning about the crucial components of linear equations. They discovered how the slope 'm' affected the steepness of the line, while the y-intercept 'b' set the starting point of the line on the y-axis.

One afternoon, while assisting a marketplace vendor, Leo noticed an intriguing pattern in the pricing of apples. "Look at this," he gestured towards the price tags. "The price increases by the same amount for each additional pound!"

The friends quickly gathered around the apple crate. Alex, with a piece of chalk in hand, scribbled on a wooden crate. "Let's let 'y' represent the total cost in dollars and 'x' be the number of pounds of apples. Then, we can write the equation $y = 2x$. Here, the coefficient '2' represents the rate at which the total cost increases for each additional pound of apples. This, my friends, is a linear equation!"

Excitement filled the air as they realized the real-world application of linear equations. They plotted the equation on a makeshift graph and marveled at the emerging straight line.

Over the following weeks, the friends refined their skills in creating and solving linear equations. They learned to solve for 'x' when 'y' was given, interpret the meaning of the slope and y-intercept in real-world scenarios, and find the equation of a line given two points.

Their understanding of Linear Equations faced a real challenge when a locked chest materialized before them bearing a cryptic note: "Find the key that lies where the two lines meet." The chest was inscribed with two equations: $y = 2x + 1$ and $y = -x + 3$.

Priya's eyes widened in recognition. "This is a system of linear equations," she exclaimed. "We need to find the point where these two lines intersect."

"Right," Leo nodded, "And that means we're looking for the 'x' and 'y' values that satisfy both equations."

The friends gathered around a makeshift drawing of the two lines on the ground. Mia traced the lines with her finger, "When we set the two equations equal to each other, we're essentially finding the point 'x' where the 'y' values of both equations match."

"Using a piece of chalk, Alex started to write on the wooden crate they were using as a makeshift table, "So, let's set $2x + 1$ equal to $-x + 3$ to find the 'x' value. That gives us $3x = 2$, so $x = 2/3$."

Priya picked up the chalk next, "And then we substitute $x = 2/3$ into either equation to find 'y'. If we put it in the first equation, we get $y = 2*(2/3) + 1$, which simplifies to $y = 7/3$."

The friends collectively held their breath as Alex wrote the final coordinates on the crate. "(2/3, 7/3)," he declared.

"Those are the coordinates of the intersection!" Mia exclaimed. As soon as they announced the solution, the chest sprung open, revealing a key. The friends cheered as they realized they had successfully used their understanding of linear equations to solve a real-world problem."

Upon declaring the solution, the chest sprung open revealing a key. They had navigated through the world of linear equations and successfully applied their knowledge to solve the challenge. The friends were left exhilarated, eagerly anticipating their next mathematical adventure.

Their journey had equipped them with a newfound appreciation for mathematics. The bustling marketplace of Linear City, filled with commerce and vendor negotiations, had given them a practical perspective. They now saw math as more than a school subject; it was a tool that permeated their everyday lives.

Satisfied with their victory, they began their journey back to the classroom, carrying with them the excitement for their next mathematical exploration: Systems of Linear Equations. The interplay of multiple lines, equations, and shared solutions was something they couldn't wait to unravel.

As they teleported back to their classroom, the friends wore content smiles, ready to face the next mathematical challenge.

CHAPTER 13 OVERVIEW

Concepts Covered

- **LINEAR EQUATIONS:** This chapter revisited linear equations, which are equations that form a straight line when graphed.
- **SOLVING LINEAR EQUATIONS:** The adventurers explored different methods for solving linear equations, including graphing, substitution, and elimination.
- **APPLICATIONS OF LINEAR EQUATIONS:** The chapter covered how linear equations can model various real-world situations.

Practical Applications

Linear equations are fundamental in many fields, such as physics, economics, and social sciences. They can be used to model and solve problems involving constant rates of change, such as velocity, cost, and income.

Key Equations or Formulas

The standard form of a linear equation is $Ax + By = C$, where A, B, and C are constants, and A and B are not both zero.

The slope-intercept form of a linear equation is $y = mx + b$, where m represents the slope and b is the y-intercept of the line.

Practice Problems

1. The friends visit a market where they find a vendor selling magical potions. The vendor has a sign that says, "The cost of the potions increases by $5 for each additional potion." If the cost of one potion is $10, can you write a linear equation that models this situation? What is the cost of 4 potions?

2. In Linear City, Leo observes a beautiful tower. He notices that as he moves 3 steps away from the tower, the tower appears to be 2 units shorter. If the tower appears to be 20 units tall when Leo is standing right next to it, can you write a linear equation that describes this scenario? How tall does the tower appear when Leo is 9 steps away?

3. Mia sees a clothes shop in Linear City and is interested in a dress. The shop offers a discount of $10 for each additional dress purchased. If the price of one dress is $50, write an equation that models this situation. What would be the price of 3 dresses?

4. Priya finds a game stall in the market. In this game, the score increases by 15 points for each successful attempt. If Priya has 20 points after her first successful attempt, write a linear equation to represent this scenario. How many points would Priya have after 5 successful attempts?

Solutions

1. The linear equation that models the situation is $y = 5*(x-1)+10$, where 'y' represents the total cost and 'x' is the number of potions bought. If you plug in $x = 4$, the equation becomes $y = 5*(4-1) + 10$, so $y = 25$. Thus, the cost of 4 potions would be $25.

2. The linear equation is $y = -2x + 20$, where 'y' represents the apparent height of the tower and 'x' is the number of steps Leo takes. Plugging $x = 9$ into the equation gives us $y = -2*9 + 20$, so $y = 2$. Thus, the tower would appear to be 2 units tall when Leo is 9 steps away.

3. If the first dress costs $50, and each subsequent dress costs $10 less, the total cost of x dresses would be given by the equation: $y = 50x - 10(x - 1)$ where y is the total cost, and x is the number of dresses. So, for 3 dresses, the total cost would be: $y = 50*3 - 10*(3 - 1) = \$130$.

4. The linear equation is $y = 15x + 5$, where 'y' is the total score and 'x' is the number of successful attempts. If you plug in $x = 5$, the equation becomes $y = 15 * 5 + 5$, so $y = 80$. Therefore, Priya would have 80 points after 5 successful attempts.

CHAPTER 14

Equationopolis - the City of Rational Equations

It was a new day at school and the group's environment shifted abruptly. The familiar surroundings of their classroom faded, and in its place emerged a bustling cityscape, magnificent in its complexity and grandeur. The city's architecture was intricate and mathematical, its symmetry suggesting the work of a master mathematician. Above the city gates, a grand sign proudly announced, "Welcome to Equationopolis - the City of Rational Equations."

Emerging from the scientific calculator, Mr. Euler greeted them with an inviting wave, his eyes sparkling with anticipation. "Welcome, young explorers, to Equationopolis, where rational equations rule the roost!"

"Rational equations?" Leo echoed, glancing up at the towering structures with a quizzical expression. "Are these equations supposed to be...reasonable?"

Mr. Euler let out a hearty laugh. "That's a creative interpretation, Leo! However, in the world of mathematics, rational equations are equations that involve fractions where the top and bottom parts - what we call the numerators and denominators - are polynomials."

In the subsequent days, the adventurers embarked on an exploratory journey into the heart of rational equations. They came to understand that 'rational' was a term linked to 'ratio.' As such, rational equations were essentially ratios of polynomials, and to dissect these equations, they needed to grasp some key principles.

"Alright, adventurers," Mr. Euler began, "To solve rational equations, we need to start by finding a common denominator for the fractions."

Mia frowned thoughtfully at this. "So, if we have an equation like $x/3 + x/4 = 1$, our common denominator would be...12?"

"Exactly!" Mr. Euler replied, pleased at Mia's quick understanding. "And once we have a common denominator, our next step is to get rid of the fractions."

Leo considered this, his brows furrowed in concentration. "That means we multiply each term by the common denominator, right? Like in our example, we'd multiply each term by 12?"

"Spot on, Leo!" Mr. Euler affirmed. "This process, known as clearing the fractions, transforms the equation into a simpler one which we can solve more easily."

As the days turned into weeks, the friends worked tirelessly on numerous rational equations. Their understanding deepened as they practiced finding shared denominators, multiplying each term of the equation by this denominator to eliminate fractions, and subsequently solving the equation that ensued.

Amidst this exploration, they came across a challenging real-world problem. Equationopolis was divided into several districts, each with its unique water requirements.

However, the city's water distribution system was malfunctioning. The engineers were at their wit's end trying to distribute water evenly to all districts. Sensing an opportunity to apply their newfound knowledge, the friends offered to help.

They spent long hours with the engineers, studying the city's blueprints and crafting a rational equation to tackle the water distribution problem. The city had three districts. The first district needed one-third of the water supply, the second needed a quarter, and the third district required the rest.

"If we consider 'x' as the total water supply, and 'y' as the amount for the third district, we can write the equation as $\frac{1}{3}x + \frac{1}{4}x + y = x$," Priya proposed, her hand moving swiftly over a piece of parchment.
"We just need to solve for 'y'," Leo noted, studying Priya's work intently.

"Right," Mia concurred. "And to do that, we'll first need to simplify the fractions and then rearrange the equation."

Working together, they carefully solved the equation. It was no small task, but by following the steps they'd learned, they determined that y equaled $\frac{5}{12}x$. This suggested that the third district should receive five-twelfths of the total water supply for fair distribution.

Upon presenting their solution to the city's engineers, the initial skepticism from the experts faded into awe.

The engineers adjusted the water distribution valves according to the group's solution. As the water began to flow evenly into each district, the engineer's disbelief transformed into respect and admiration.

Their successful application of rational equations had not only solved a crucial problem but also earned them the gratitude of Equationopolis's inhabitants. As they continued to explore the city, they knew that they had made a tangible difference using mathematics.

The sudden appearance of a new scroll caught their attention. "Prepare for an uncertain future" it read, hinting at their next mathematical adventure.

CHAPTER 14 OVERVIEW

Concepts Covered

- **RATIONAL EQUATIONS:** In this chapter, our adventurers were introduced to rational equations. These are equations that contain fractions whose numerators and/or denominators are polynomials.
- **SOLVING RATIONAL EQUATIONS:** Our young scholars learned how to solve rational equations. This involves finding a common denominator, using it to clear the fractions, and then solving the resulting equation.

Practical Applications

The friends used their knowledge of rational equations to solve a real-world problem in the city of Equationopolis. They successfully balanced the water supply among different districts of the city, showing how rational equations can be used to represent and solve problems involving proportional relationships in real life.

Key Equations or Formulas

The equation that the group came up with to solve the water distribution problem in Equationopolis was $\frac{1}{3}x + \frac{1}{4}x + y = x$. This equation shows the relationship between the total water supply (x) and the amount of water needed for the third district (y). After solving, they found that $y = \frac{5}{12}x$, which means the third district should receive $\frac{5}{12}$ of the total water supply for fair distribution.

Practice Problems

1. The adventurers found a treasure chest that can only be opened by solving the following rational equation: $2/x + 3/(x - 2) = 5/(2x - 4)$. Solve this equation to help them open the chest.

2. The city of Equationopolis has four districts with varying electricity needs. The first district requires $\frac{1}{4}$ of the total electricity, the second district needs $\frac{1}{5}$, and the third needs $\frac{1}{6}$. Write a rational equation that represents this scenario if 'x' is the total electricity supply and 'y' is the amount the fourth district gets.

3. While exploring Equationopolis, the adventurers stumbled upon a bakery that sells pies. A whole pie costs $14, but the bakery also sells half pies for $8 each. If Leo buys 'x' whole pies and 'y' half pies, create a rational equation that represents the total cost. Solve this equation for y if Leo has a total of $50 to spend and decides to buy 2 whole pies.

4. The adventurers are trying to solve a riddle that states: "The sum of the reciprocals of two consecutive numbers is $^{17}\!/_{72}$. Find the numbers." Help the adventurers solve this riddle.

Solutions

1. To solve the rational equation, we need to find a common denominator. The common denominator for x, x-2, and 2x-4 is 2x(x-2), so we multiply each term by that. Doing so, we get:

22(x-2) + 32x = 5x

This simplifies to:
4x - 8 + 6x = 5x
Solving this for x gives:
x = 8

2. The rational equation would be:

   $\frac{1}{4}x + \frac{1}{5}x + \frac{1}{6}x + y = x$

   Combining the fractions on the left-hand side, we get:

   $(15x + 12x + 10x) / 60x + y = x$

   This simplifies to:

   $37x / 60x + y = x$

   Therefore, y represents the remainder of the total electricity after the first three districts have received their shares.

3. The total cost for Leo's purchase is represented by:

   $14x + 8y = 50$

   If Leo decides to buy 2 whole pies (x = 2), the equation becomes:

   $14*2 + 8y = 50$

   Solving for y, we get: y = 2.25

   So, Leo can buy 2 whole pies and 2.25 half pies with $50. Since Leo can't buy a fraction of a pie, we can assume he buys 2 half pies and will have some money left over.

4. Let's say the two consecutive numbers are n and n+1. The equation becomes:

$1/n + 1/(n+1) = 17/72$

After finding a common denominator, the equation becomes:

$(2n + 1) / n(n + 1) = 17/72$

Cross multiplying gives:

$72(2n + 1) = 17n(n + 1)$

This simplifies to a quadratic equation:

$17n^2 - 137n + 72 = 0$

Solving this quadratic equation, we get n = 8 or n = -9/8. Since n must be positive and we are looking for whole numbers, we discard the solution n = -9/8.

Therefore, the two consecutive numbers are 8 and 9.

CHAPTER 15

Journey into the Metropolis of Uncertainty

Bidding farewell to the orderly precision of Equationopolis, a flurry of colors enveloped Mia, Priya, Leo, and Mr. Euler. The whirlwind of hues eventually subsided, revealing a new destination – a bustling city with a vibrant, eclectic vibe. Marketplaces brimmed with life, stalls offering games of chance attracted the young and old, and a grand central arena echoed with excited chatter.

"Welcome to the Metropolis of Uncertainty – the City of Chance," a banner overhead proudly declared.

"Well, we're definitely not in Equationopolis anymore," Mia chuckled, gazing at the hustle and bustle.

"You're right, Mia," Mr. Euler said with a twinkle in his eyes. "This city is the heart of Probability and Data Analysis."

Over the next few days, as they explored the city, they

dove into the study of probability, starting with simple concepts.

"The probability of an event happening," Mr. Euler explained, "is the number of ways it can happen divided by the total number of outcomes."

They practiced with coins, understanding that the chance of getting a head or a tail in a fair coin toss was equal – a 1 out of 2 probability, or 0.5 when expressed as a decimal.

"In the same way," Leo observed, "rolling a die has six outcomes, so the probability of rolling any number is 1 out of 6."

The friends spent hours calculating probabilities of different events, using coins, dice, and even drawing cards from a deck.

Their exploration took them deeper into the realm of probability, where they encountered more complex concepts such as dependent and independent events, and the intriguing field of statistics and data analysis. Mr. Euler explained how data could be collected, represented, and analyzed to gain meaningful insights.

They practiced creating frequency tables, pie charts, and histograms. They also learned about the measures of central tendency: mean, median, and mode.

As their understanding grew, they found themselves drawn to the city's central arena. Here, spectators eagerly watched games of chance, with winnings calculated based on the probabilities of certain outcomes. The friends couldn't resist the opportunity to apply their newly acquired knowledge.

Their first game was the spinning wheel. It was divided into four equal parts: red, blue, green, and yellow. "If we bet on red," Mia proposed, "what's the chance we'll win?"

"Each color has an equal chance of being landed on," Priya replied, calculating quickly. "So the probability is 1 out of 4, or 0.25 as a decimal."

Their prediction was correct, and when the spinner landed on red, the crowd roared in approval. The friends celebrated, their understanding of simple probability reinforced.

The following game involved two dice. Priya suggested, "What if we calculate the probability of the sum of the numbers being seven?"

"Well," said Leo, "there are 6 possibilities: 1 and 6, 2 and 5, 3 and 4, 4 and 3, 5 and 2, or 6 and 1."

"And," Mr. Euler added, "since each die has six faces, there are a total of 6 times 6, or 36 possibilities. So, the probability is 6 out of 36, which simplifies to 1 out of 6." As they anticipated, a seven was rolled, and their prediction was validated once again.

Their consistent success attracted the attention of the mayor, a formidable woman with a keen intellect. She invited them to the city hall, posing a challenge: "We're collecting vast amounts of data on the visitors and residents of our city. Can you help us analyze it?"

Excitedly, they accepted the challenge. Mia suggested, "First, we need to clean this data, removing any irrelevant information." They then proceeded to organize the data, using frequency tables, and represented it visually in pie charts and histograms.

Taking the cleaned data, the group decided to create a frequency table first. Leo explained, "A frequency table is a simple way to represent data. It's basically a table that shows how often each value, or range of values, appears in our data set." With a set of data involving the ages of the city's residents, they created a frequency table that indicated how many people belonged to different age brackets. The table provided a quick, easy-to-understand snapshot of the age distribution in the city.

Next, they tackled visual representations. "Pie charts are excellent for displaying data in proportions," Priya pointed out. Using the same age data, they made a pie chart that showed the proportion of the city's residents that fell into each age bracket. The chart's 'slices' represented each age group, their size relative to the whole 'pie' displaying the proportion of the total population that each group comprised.

"Histograms, on the other hand," Mia added, "are great for showing frequency distributions." They took a set of data regarding the heights of the city's residents and made a histogram. The horizontal axis represented height ranges, while the vertical axis represented the number of individuals falling into each range. The taller the bar on the histogram, the more individuals in that height range.

Together, the frequency table, pie chart, and histogram provided diverse views of the data, each offering different insights. The officials could now clearly see the age and height distributions within the city, a useful basis for planning and decision-making.

"Now, we can calculate the mean, median, and mode of the data to get a better understanding of the trends," Priya added.

"Calculating the mean, median, and mode is a fundamental part of data analysis," Priya started. "Let's start with the mean, which is simply the average of all the numbers in a data set. To calculate it, we add up all the numbers and then divide by how many numbers there are. It's the sum of all data points divided by the count of data points."

She scribbled a few numbers on a piece of paper. "For example, if our data set is the numbers 2, 3, and 5, the mean would be (2+3+5)/3, which equals 10/3, or approximately 3.33."

She continued, "The median, on the other hand, is the middle value in a data set when the numbers are listed in numerical order. If there's an even number of data points, then the median is the average of the two middle numbers. For instance, in our previous data set of 2, 3, and 5, the median is 3 since it's the middle number. However, if our data set was 2, 3, 4, and 5, the median would be (3+4)/2, which equals 3.5, because there are two middle numbers, 3 and 4."

"Finally," Priya said, picking up her piece of paper again, "the mode is the number that appears most frequently in a data set. It's possible to have one mode, more than one mode, or no mode at all. For instance, in the data set 2, 2, 3, 5, 5, the modes are 2 and 5 because they both appear twice, which is more often than the other number, 3."

"Through the mean, median, and mode," Priya concluded, "we can gain different perspectives on the data set and better understand its distribution and tendencies."

"Wow, great explanation Priya, thank you!" said Leo.

They showed the officials how to interpret these visuals, drawing conclusions from the data, and making informed decisions.

After days of intense work, they left the city hall, their faces glowing with satisfaction. Their knowledge of probability and data analysis had helped the city officials immensely, and they felt proud of their accomplishment. Their exploration in the Metropolis of Uncertainty was both fun-filled and educative. Their understanding of probability, statistics, and data analysis had deepened, and they felt confident in using these skills in real-world situations. As they prepared to leave, the sight of the city's vibrant markets, the echoes of the lively arena, and their fruitful time spent in the city hall brought a sense of fulfillment.

Their next adventure awaited, and the parchment before them hinted at their next destination: "Next Stop, the Balancing Cities". Ready to dive into a new world of mathematical concepts, they ventured forth, the City of Chance fading behind them, replaced by the promise of new learning and more adventures.

CHAPTER 15 OVERVIEW

Concepts Covered

- **PROBABILITY:** This chapter introduced the concept of probability, a measure of the likelihood that a particular event will occur. The adventurers delved into the calculation of simple probabilities and understood the concept of independent and dependent events.
- **DATA ANALYSIS:** The adventurers learned about data analysis, which involves collecting, organizing, cleaning, and interpreting data. They also explored frequency tables, pie charts, histograms, and measures of central tendency: mean, median, and mode.
- **CHANCE:** They explored how probability and data analysis are used to understand and predict outcomes in games of chance, applying their skills in the city's central arena.

Practical Applications

Probability and data analysis are critical in many real-world scenarios, including predicting weather patterns, determining insurance rates, understanding odds in games of chance, and making informed decisions based on data. The adventurers used these concepts to navigate the unpredictable City of Chance and aid the city officials in analyzing their data.

Key Equations or Formulas

The basic formula for probability is $P(E)$ = number of favorable outcomes / total number of outcomes. In data analysis, measures of central tendency were introduced, with the mean calculated as the sum of all data points divided by the number of data points, the median as the middle value in an ordered data set, and the mode as the most frequently occurring data point(s).

Practice Problems

1. Let's go back to the spinner game! Mia has a spinner with four equally sized sections colored red, blue, yellow, and green. If she spins the spinner once, what is the probability that it will land on blue?

2. Back to the dice game! If Leo rolls a standard six-sided die, what is the probability that he will roll an even number?

3. The mayor of the City of Chance handed the adventurers a data set of the number of visitors to the city over ten days: 50, 55, 48, 52, 58, 49, 51, 54, 56, 53. Can you help them find the mean, median, and mode of this data set?

4. The city officials are planning a new event and have been observing the weather patterns. Over the past 30 days, it rained on 12 days. Based on this data, what's the probability that it will rain on the day of the event?

Solutions

1. Since there are four equally sized sections on the spinner and only one of them is blue, the probability of the spinner landing on blue is 1 out of 4, or 1/4.

2. On a standard six-sided die, there are three even numbers: 2, 4, and 6. Therefore, the probability of rolling an even number is 3 out of 6, which simplifies to 1/2.

3. To find the mean of the dataset, you add up all the numbers and then divide by the count of numbers. The sum of the numbers is 526, and there are 10 numbers. So, the mean is 526/10 = 52.6.

To find the median, you list the numbers in numerical order and then find the middle number. If there's an even number of numbers, you take the average of the two middle numbers. The ordered list is 48, 49, 50, 51, 52, 53, 54, 55, 56, 58. The two middle numbers are 52 and 53, so the median is (52+53)/2 = 52.5.

The mode is the number that appears most frequently. In this data set, no number repeats, so there is no mode.

4. If it rained on 12 out of 30 days, then the probability of it raining on any given day (assuming each day is independent and equally likely) is 12/30, which simplifies to 2/5 or 40%.

CHAPTER 16

Systems of Equations and the Balancing Cities

The adventure continued as the team bid farewell to the City of Chance, their next destination awaiting them. As another parchment fluttered down, they read, "Explore the harmonious balance of equations in the Twin Cities of Balance." As soon as they finished reading, the world blurred, and they landed in the heart of two separate yet interwoven cities.

Mr. Euler gestured towards the cities. "These cities, though distinct, work together in harmony. Their survival depends on constant balance and exchange, a living example of systems of equations - where we solve multiple conditions simultaneously."

The first city, vibrant and green, was a hub of agriculture and manufacturing, while the second city bustled with markets, taking care of trade and distribution. For these cities to thrive, they needed to balance production and distribution perfectly, creating a living example of systems of equations.

Their first encounter in the manufacturing city was with a group of farmers led by a sturdy farmer named Jeb. He approached the group, concern in his eyes, "We grow wheat and corn, but it's a constant struggle to decide the area for each to meet the city's demands."

A sense of purpose lit Mia's eyes, "This is a perfect scenario for a system of linear equations. We'll help you find that balance."

Surrounding a table strewn with crop data and city demands, they began their task. Mia initiated the process, "We'll let 'x' represent the area for wheat and 'y' for corn."

Leo picked up from there, "So, if all land is divided between wheat or corn, the first equation can be $x + y =$ total farming area."

"And if the city requires twice as much wheat as corn," Lena jumped in, "we can express this requirement as our second equation: $x = 2y$."

They patiently explained to the farmers how these equations mirrored their situation and how they could solve them using two methods: substitution and elimination.

"Substitution involves rearranging one equation to

express one variable in terms of the other," explained Leo. "Then this expression is substituted into the other equation. For example, from x = 2y, we substitute 'x' in the first equation to get 2y + y = total farming area."

"Elimination, on the other hand," he continued, "involves manipulating the equations such that when they are added or subtracted, one variable is eliminated. For example, if we multiply the second equation by -1, we get -x = -2y. Adding this to the first equation results in y = total farming area, eliminating 'x'."

Using these methods, they found the ideal balance of wheat and corn to plant. Seeing the logic unfold, Jeb and his fellow farmers were awestruck. "We've been playing a guessing game for years. This is a revelation!"

Next, they made their way to the city of trade, where they met a group of traders led by a woman named Selena. The traders, just like the farmers, had a problem of balance - different goods needed to reach various parts of the city in the most efficient way.

As Mia proposed using systems of equations to determine the optimal routes, the team dug into understanding the trade routes and formulating equations. This system was more complex than the farmers' situation, but the principles of substitution and elimination held just as true.

Working with Selena's trading team, Leo sketched out a rudimentary map of the city and the different destinations for the goods on a piece of parchment. "Let's label the destinations as A, B, and C, and the amount of goods for each as x, y, and z, respectively," he suggested.

Selena looked at the diagram and provided additional information. "We need twice as much goods at B as at A, and C requires the total amount of goods delivered to A and B."

"Aha!" exclaimed Mia. "Those conditions give us two equations. If we have twice as much at B as at A, we can write it as $y = 2x$. And if C requires the total amount of goods delivered to A and B, that would be $z = x + y$."

"Perfect," Lena chimed in. "And we know that the total amount of goods we can transport in a day is a fixed number, let's call it T. That gives us our third equation: $x + y + z = T$."

Leo laid out the system of equations clearly on the parchment, and they collectively explained to Selena and her team how each equation represented a piece of their logistics puzzle. Then, they proceeded to solve it using substitution and elimination methods.

"Substitution here involves replacing 'y' and 'z' in the third equation with their expressions from the other two equations," Leo detailed. "We would have $x + 2x + x + 2x = T$, simplifying to $5x = T$. Then, $x = T/5$."
"For elimination," Lena continued, "we can start by substituting $y = 2x$ into the third equation: $x + 2x + z = T$, which simplifies to $3x + z = T$. Next, we substitute z from the second equation, $z = x + y$, into this equation to get $3x + x + 2x = T$."

"We simplify that to get $6x = T$, and solve for x to find $x = T/6$," Leo added, doing the calculations on a piece of parchment for everyone to see.

"Next, we substitute $x = T/6$ back into $y = 2x$ to find $y = T/3$, and into $z = x + y$ to find $z = T/2$," Mia concluded, pointing at each step on the parchment.

Upon reaching the solutions, they saw that all quantities of goods to be delivered were proportionate to the total capacity. Selena looked over the results, her eyes wide with surprise. "By the stars... That's the most efficient distribution I've ever seen. We've been muddling through without realizing the solution was in the math. Thank you, adventurers!"

During their weeks in the Twin Cities, the adventurers witnessed firsthand the immense versatility of systems of equations, solving problems of varying complexity. Through this, they gained a deep understanding of systems of equations and their practical applications.

As they prepared to leave, they carried with them not only the mathematical knowledge of systems of equations, the concepts of substitution and elimination, but also the profound understanding of how these mathematical principles could bring harmony and balance in real-life situations. Emboldened, they set their sights on their next destination, ready to face any mathematical challenges that lay ahead.

CHAPTER 16 OVERVIEW

Concepts Covered

- **SYSTEMS OF EQUATIONS:** A mathematical framework that enables the simultaneous solving of multiple equations containing multiple variables.
- **ELIMINATION METHOD:** A technique used in solving systems of equations by adding or subtracting the equations in a way that eliminates one of the variables.
- **SUBSTITUTION METHOD:** A method for solving systems of equations where one equation is solved for one variable in terms of the other, and this expression is then substituted into the other equation.

Practical Applications

Systems of equations are used in various fields, such as physics, engineering, business, and economics, to solve problems where multiple conditions are simultaneously met.

Key Equations or Formulas

For a system of equations in two variables x and y:

Equation 1: $a_1x + b_1y = c_1$
Equation 2: $a_2x + b_2y = c_2$

The solutions are the values of x and y that satisfy both equations.

The two main methods to solve such a system are substitution and elimination:

Substitution involves solving one of the equations for one variable and then substituting this expression into the other equation.

Elimination involves adding or subtracting the equations in order to eliminate one of the variables, making it possible to solve for the other.

Practice Problems

1. <u>Farming Fun:</u> Let's say there are two fruit farms. Farm A produces 5 oranges and 3 apples, earning $23 in a day. Farm B produces 2 oranges and 4 apples, earning $20 in a day. How much does each orange and each apple earn?

2. <u>Planting Puzzles:</u> Lena has 100 square meters of land to plant carrots and potatoes. She wants to plant twice as many square meters of potatoes as carrots. Can you write a system of equations to represent this situation and solve it to find out how many square meters Lena should use for each crop?

3. <u>Trade Route Troubles:</u> Leo is planning trade routes for distributing goods. Route A takes 2 hours to the city of manufacturing and 3 hours to the city of trade. Route B takes 3 hours to the city of manufacturing and 2 hours to the city of trade. If he has 15 hours for deliveries, how many trips can he make on each route? Write and solve a system of equations for this problem.

4. <u>Equation Excursion:</u> Can you solve this system of equations using the substitution method?

$2x + 3y = 18$
$4x = y + 2$

Solutions

1.   The two farms create a system of equations where the number of oranges (x) and apples (y) corresponds to the total earnings of each farm.

Farm A: $5x + 3y = \$23$
Farm B: $2x + 4y = \$20$

By multiplying the first equation by 2 and the second by 5, we can use the elimination method to solve for y (apples), and then substitute y into one of the original equations to find x (oranges).

Doing the calculations gives x = $3 (price of each orange) and y = $4 (price of each apple).

2.   Planting Puzzles: This is solved through substitution. If we let c represent the area for carrots and p represent the area for potatoes, we have:

$c + p = 100$
$p = 2c$

Substituting the second equation into the first gives us $c + 2c = 100$, or $3c = 100$. Solving for c gives us c = 33.33 (rounded to the nearest hundredth). Substituting c = 33.33 into p = 2c gives us p = 66.67. So, Lena should plant approximately 33.33 square meters of carrots and approximately 66.67 square meters of potatoes.

3.   Trade Route Troubles: Let a represent the number of trips on Route A and b represent the number of trips on Route B. We have:

$2a + 3b = 15$
$3a + 2b = 15$

Multiplying the first equation by 2 and the second equation by 3 gives:

$4a + 6b = 30$
$9a + 6b = 45$

Subtracting the first equation from the second gives $5a = 15$ or $a = 3$. Substituting $a = 3$ into the first equation gives $b = 3$. So, Leo can make 3 trips on each route.

4.   Equation Excursion: The correct solution should be:

We can solve the system using substitution:

$2x + 3y = 18$
$4x = y + 2$

We can rewrite the second equation as $y = 4x - 2$ and substitute it into the first equation: $2x + 3(4x - 2) = 18$, which simplifies to $14x = 24$, or $x = 24/14 \approx 1.71$ (rounded to the nearest hundredth). Substituting $x = 1.71$ into $y = 4x - 2$ gives us $y \approx 4.84$. So, the solution is $x \approx 1.71$, $y \approx 4.84$.

CHAPTER 17

Inequalities and the Great Balancing Act

Mia, Priya and Leo walked together to school as they did every day. But today wasn't any ordinary day—although lately they had stopped expecting ordinary!

"Look!" exclaimed Priya. "It looks like some sort of portal."

The friends tentatively walked closer towards the colorful, swirling mass that was in front of them. Leo was the first to step forward and within a millisecond, he was gone.

"Woah," said Mia nervously. "Should we go after him?!"

Without hesitation, Priya grabbed Mia and jumped straight into the portal. She wasn't afraid of anything these days.

As the shimmering portal closed behind them, Mia, Priya

and Leo found themselves standing in the heart of a bustling metropolis. Mr Euler was there too, of course. High above, billboards flashed colorful lights, and the air buzzed with the energy of a thousand conversations. A parchment floated down to them, reading, "Welcome to the Metropolis of Inequalities."

Mr. Euler's eyes sparkled with excitement. "Inequalities! They are the heart of balance. They express the idea that one quantity can be greater than or less than another. And this city, my dear friends, is the perfect place to explore them."

As they ventured deeper into the city, they found themselves in front of an imposing building: the city's central bank. The bank manager, a stern man named Mr. Gauss, greeted them with a worried frown. He had a problem: how to distribute money in such a way that each of the city's districts got at least a certain amount, but no district could receive more than a certain limit to maintain fairness.

"This sounds like a job for inequalities!" Mia piped up, her eyes sparkling with excitement. "We can use 'x' to represent the amount of money each district receives. Each district must receive at least a, but no more than b. So, our inequality would be $a \le x \le b$."

Mr. Gauss looked puzzled. "That sounds reasonable, but how do we find the right balance?"

The friends sat down with him, pens and papers spread out before them. Priya began to explain, "See, the beauty of inequalities is that they don't give a single answer. Instead, they provide a range of possible answers. So, 'x' can be any amount between 'a' and 'b'. This gives us the flexibility to adjust the distribution as needed, while ensuring it stays within the specified bounds."

For the rest of the day, they worked with Mr. Gauss, adjusting and readjusting the distributions, using the inequality as a guide. As they worked, they explained the concept further, discussing how inequalities were a tool for achieving balance and fairness, while providing a range of possibilities to work with. Mr. Gauss was thrilled with their help, and by the end of the day, each district had received a fair distribution of funds.

The next day, the friends found themselves in the city's bustling market square. A group of vendors approached them, each holding a variety of goods. The vendors wanted to price their goods in a way that would earn them a decent profit but would also attract customers.

Leo thought for a moment, then suggested, "Let's use inequalities again. If 'p' represents the price of an item, then you want to ensure the price is high enough to cover costs, say 'c', but not so high that customers won't buy it, say 'm'. So, our inequality would be $c \leq p \leq m$."

The vendors nodded, intrigued by the idea. Over the course of the day, the friends worked with each vendor, using inequalities to set a range of acceptable prices for each item. As they worked, they explained how inequalities could help strike a balance between making a profit and attracting customers.

"See, if you price your goods too high, customers won't buy them," Priya explained to a vendor.

"But if you price them too low, you won't make a profit. Inequalities allow us to find a range of prices that work for both us and the customers."

As the day wore on, the friends worked with the vendors to apply the concept of inequalities to various aspects of their businesses, from pricing to inventory management.

The vendors were delighted with their newfound understanding, and the shoppers were happy with the fair prices.

After saying their goodbyes to the vendors, the friends decided to take one last stroll through the Metropolis of Inequalities before returning to their own world. As they wandered through the city, they came across a peculiar building with the sign "Scientific Laboratory of Theoretical Hypothesis", or SLoTH for short.

Inside the building, a woman named Dr. Absolute was frantically trying to maintain the temperature of a delicate chemical reaction. The temperature needed to be controlled within a certain range around a central point to prevent the experiment from failing.

"I need the temperature to stay within 3 degrees of 70," Dr. Absolute explained. "If the temperature gets either too high or too low, the reaction will become unstable!"

Priya snapped her fingers. "This sounds like a perfect scenario for absolute value inequalities!"

Seeing the puzzled expression on Dr. Absolute's face, Leo began to explain. "If we let 't' represent the actual temperature, we want to find all possible temperatures 't' such that the difference between 't' and 70 is less than or equal to 3 degrees. We can express this as an absolute value inequality: $|t - 70| \leq 3$."

Dr. Absolute nodded, understanding dawning on her face. "That makes perfect sense! This inequality represents the range of acceptable temperatures for my experiment. The temperature needs to be within 3 degrees of 70, either above or below. So the solutions to this inequality would be the temperatures that satisfy these conditions."

With the help of their new friend, Mia, Priya, and Leo were able to calibrate the laboratory's temperature control system to keep the temperature within the desired range. Their understanding of absolute value inequalities had saved Dr. Absolute's experiment.

The rest of the day was spent in the laboratory, helping Dr. Absolute understand the practical applications of absolute value inequalities and ensuring the temperature of the experiment stayed within the specified range. As they worked, they found even more ways to apply the concepts of inequalities to problems in the laboratory, further solidifying their understanding.

The experience in the laboratory was a fitting end to their adventure in the Metropolis of Inequalities. They had not only learned about the power of inequalities but had also seen their practical applications in various scenarios, from banking and trade to scientific experiments. As they stepped back into the portal, they carried with them a deeper understanding of the balance, flexibility, and fairness offered by inequalities. They were more ready than ever to face the next mathematical challenges that lay ahead.

As the sun set on their time in the Metropolis of Inequalities, the friends reflected on their experiences. They had seen firsthand how inequalities could bring balance and fairness to different scenarios. They had helped a bank manager distribute funds fairly, and they had helped vendors price their goods in a way that benefited both them and their customers. They had seen how inequalities could provide a range of possibilities, offering flexibility and balance.

And they had shared these insights, helping the people of the Metropolis of Inequalities understand and apply these concepts in their own lives.

As they prepared to leave, Mia turned to her friends. "Inequalities are more than just mathematical expressions," she said. "They are tools for fairness, balance, and flexibility. They are a way to understand and navigate the world around us. And that, I think, is the real treasure we've found here."

With that, the friends stepped into the portal, ready to face the next adventure on their mathematical journey.

CHAPTER 17 OVERVIEW

Concepts Covered

- **COMPOUND INEQUALITIES:** A compound inequality is two simple inequalities connected by "and" (meaning both must be true) or "or" (meaning at least one must be true).
- **ABSOLUTE VALUE INEQUALITIES:** An absolute value inequality involves a variable within an absolute value symbol and is solved by creating two separate inequalities, one for the positive and one for the negative potential of the variable's value.

Practical Applications

Inequalities are widely used in various fields, such as engineering, economics, business, and medicine, to express constraints or limitations. Our adventurers used these concepts to balance the various elements of their environment in their adventure.

Key Equations or Formulas

For an inequality in one variable x:

Inequality: $ax + b \leq c$ or $ax + b \geq c$

Compound Inequality: $a < x < b$ or $x < a$ or $x > b$

Absolute Value Inequality: $|x - a| \leq b$ or $|x - a| \geq b$

Practice Problems

1. A friendly dragon will only share its gold if you're older than 12 but younger than 20. If 'x' represents your age, write this as a compound inequality.

2. A magic spell can only be cast if the wizard's power level 'p' is less than 50 but greater than 20. Write this condition as a compound inequality.

3. A potion works best when the magic ingredient 'm' is not less than 3 units away from 10. Write this condition as an absolute value inequality.

4. The Giggle Goblins only appear when the level of laughter 'L' in the town is above 50 but below 100 decibels. Write this scenario as a compound inequality.

Solutions

1. If 'x' represents your age, the compound inequality is $12 < x < 20$.
2. If 'p' represents the wizard's power level, the compound inequality is $20 < p < 50$.
3. If 'm' represents the amount of magic ingredient, the absolute value inequality is $|m - 10| \geq 3$. This can be solved as $m \geq 13$ or $m \leq 7$.
4. If 'L' represents the level of laughter, the compound inequality is $50 < L < 100$.

CHAPTER 18

Absolute Value and the
Land of Distances

As the quartet stepped out of the portal, they found themselves in a completely different setting. A flat, expansive plane stretched as far as they could see, populated by structures of different shapes, sizes, and colors. Signs of life were everywhere. People moved around, each carrying a device resembling a combination of a compass and a ruler. A large floating sign welcomed them: "Land of Distances."

The friends exchanged glances, then turned to Mr. Euler. He looked as excited as always.

"Ah! What better place to learn about absolute value than a land where distance is everything? You see, absolute value tells us the distance a number is from zero on a number line. It doesn't care about direction—only magnitude."

Mia frowned, processing this information. "But why is distance important? I mean, beyond getting from one place to another."

Mr. Euler chuckled. "That's a good question, Mia. In our world, distance helps us measure the gap between places, yes, but in mathematics, it measures the difference between values. It's used everywhere—physics, computer science, economics—you name it."

Their first encounter in this new world was with a bespectacled man named Pythagoras. He was hunched over a map, scratching his head in confusion. The map showed two cities at points A and B, and a zero point was clearly marked.

Priya peered over his shoulder. "I think we can use absolute value to solve your problem, Pythagoras. If we treat the zero point as the origin, the distances from A and B to the origin are the absolute values of A and B. So the shortest distance between A and B would be the absolute difference between these two values, or |A-B|."

Pythagoras looked at her with intrigued eyes. "That sounds promising, but could you show me how it works? I'm a visual learner."

Thus began an impromptu math class in the middle of the Land of Distances. The friends huddled around Pythagoras' map, using it as their chalkboard. They illustrated the paths from points A and B to the origin, explaining how absolute value focused only on the magnitude of the distance, not the direction.

As they continued their journey through this peculiar land, they found countless applications of absolute value. At a bustling bakery, they helped the baker calculate the difference in weight between two batches of bread using absolute value. The baker, a rotund man with flour in his hair, was initially skeptical.

Leo explained, "Think of each loaf of bread as a point on your number line. The absolute value of the difference in their weights is like the distance between these two points."

A light bulb seemed to go off in the baker's head. "So it's

not about which batch is heavier or lighter—it's about how much they differ. That's brilliant!"

Joyful with success from their bakery encounter, they pressed on. Soon, they found themselves before a crowd in the city square, where a young boy held a tablet filled with equations. Seeing their knowledge of absolute value, he asked if they could help him solve an equation on his list, which read $|x - 3| = 7$.

Mr. Euler knelt down to the boy's level. "Absolutely. The solution to an absolute value equation is where the expression inside the absolute value equals the value on the other side, or its negative. In this case, it means $x - 3$ could equal 7 or -7."

"So," Priya added, "x could be 10 or -4."

Intrigued, the boy showed them another equation. "What about $|2x + 4| < 6$? It's different, isn't it?"

"Yes, it is," Mia acknowledged. "This is an absolute value inequality. It states that the distance between $2x + 4$ and 0 should be less than 6. To solve this, we consider two scenarios: one where $2x + 4$ is less than 6 and another where $2x + 4$ is greater than -6."

After working out the math on the tablet, they found that the solution was $-5 < x < 1$. The crowd, watching the proceedings with rapt attention, broke into applause, and the quartet exchanged satisfied smiles. At a local school, they had the chance to explain absolute value to a group of students. Priya drew a number line on the chalkboard, marking the scores of two teams in a game. She showed the students how to calculate the absolute difference between the scores, emphasizing that it represented the distance between the two points on the number line.

When they finally left the Land of Distances, they had not only learned about absolute value in depth but also made a tangible difference to the people living there. As they stepped into theportal, waving goodbye, they knew they were leaving a community that had a newfound appreciation for distances and the value they held.

CHAPTER 18 OVERVIEW

Concepts Covered

- **ABSOLUTE VALUE:** Our adventurers learned about the absolute value of a number, which is its distance from zero on the number line. They learned that the absolute value is always non-negative.
- **ABSOLUTE VALUE EQUATIONS:** This includes equations where the absolute value of a variable or an expression is set equal to a number. The friends discovered how to solve these equations by creating two separate equations.
- **ABSOLUTE VALUE INEQUALITIES:** These inequalities describe a range of values for a variable or an expression, rather than a single solution. The quartet learned to solve these inequalities by considering two scenarios for the expression within the absolute value.

Practical Applications

Understanding absolute value is crucial in various real-life scenarios, such as calculating distances, determining absolute differences, and analyzing data.

Key Equations or Formulas

Absolute Value: $|x| = x$ if $x \geq 0$, and $|x| = -x$ if $x < 0$
Absolute Value Equation: $|x - a| = b$
Absolute Value Inequality: $|x - a| \leq b$ or $|x - a| \geq b$

Practice Problems

1. The magic wand in the Land of Distances only works when its charge 'c' is no less than 5 units away from 0. Write this condition as an absolute value inequality.

2. Lena finds a magical amulet, whose power 'p' varies from day to day. If the amulet's power can be anywhere from 2 units below to 5 units above 3, write an absolute value inequality to represent this.

3. At a school fair in the Land of Distances, the weight of the bags of popcorn are supposed to be 10 ounces each, but can deviate by 2 ounces. Write an absolute value equation to represent the acceptable weight range for the popcorn bags.

4. During a game of mystical darts, Leo scores 's' points. If his score can deviate by at most 3 points from 20 for him to win the game, write an absolute value inequality to represent this scenario.

Solutions

1. The magic wand works when its charge 'c' is no less than 5 units away from 0. This can be represented as the absolute value inequality $|c| \geq 5$.

2. Lena's magical amulet's power 'p' can be anywhere from 2 units below to 5 units above 3. So the absolute value inequality is $|p - 3| \leq 2$.

3. The bags of popcorn are supposed to be 10 ounces each, but can deviate by 2 ounces. Therefore, the absolute value equation is $|w - 10| \leq 2$, where 'w' is the weight of the popcorn bag.

4. In the game of mystical darts, Leo's score 's' can deviate by at most 3 points from 20. This can be represented as the absolute value inequality $|s - 20| \leq 3$.

CHAPTER 19

Inequalities and the Island of Comparison

The quartet was met by the gentle warmth of the sun as they made their way out of the portal. Their feet sank into the soft sand of a beautiful beach, where the rolling waves of a crystal-clear sea greeted them. Just off the coast, they spotted an island, a tantalizing mystery shrouded in a fine mist.

"Welcome to the Island of Comparison," Mr. Euler began, a twinkle in his eye as he pointed out towards the mystical island. "This land, my friends, will reveal the profound secrets of inequalities."

"Inequalities?" Leo inquired, squinting against the sunlight as he examined the distant island. The word hung in the air, a promise of new knowledge and adventure.

"Indeed," Mr. Euler confirmed with a nod. "Inequalities, you see, are about the relative size or value of two numbers. They allow us to understand which number is larger, smaller, or if they're unequal. Now, observe that island closely. Our challenge is to get there."

Before the team could raise their questions, they were approached by Thales, a resident of the island. As the guardian of the Island of Comparison, he explained their task: to construct a seaworthy raft using logs of varying lengths. The challenge, however, was that each log must be less than 5 feet in length to maintain the balance of the raft.

"In other words," Thales clarified, drawing a line in the sand, "if 'L' represents the length of the log, the inequality we're dealing with is $L < 5$."

Thales surprised them with another condition, "Not just the lengths, there is also a condition for the number of logs you can use!" he said. "To maintain the balance of the raft, you must use more than 10 but fewer than 15 logs." The group took a moment to digest this additional information.

Priya quickly understood, "Ah, that's a compound inequality! So, we're looking at $10 < n < 15$, where 'n' is the number of logs we can use." She quickly drew another line on the sand to represent this condition.

Mia's eyes widened with realization. "So, we can utilize any logs as long as they're shorter than 5 feet?"

"Absolutely!" Thales cheered, clapping his hands together

in affirmation. "Now, off with you. Seek out the logs that meet our inequality!"

The friends eagerly began their log hunt, scouring the beach and measuring the length of each find. Several logs failed to meet the inequality condition and had to be discarded. After a collective effort, they finally amassed enough logs that satisfied $L < 5$.

Mia's eyes widened with realization. "So, we can utilize any logs as long as they're shorter than 5 feet?"

"Absolutely!" Thales cheered, clapping his hands together in affirmation. "Now, off with you. Seek out the logs that meet our inequality!"

The friends eagerly began their log hunt, scouring the beach and measuring the length of each find. Several logs failed to meet the inequality condition and had to be discarded. After a collective effort, they finally got together enough logs that satisfied $L < 5$.

As they were about to start building the raft, Leo had an idea. He took a stick and began to draw on the sand, laying out the lengths of the logs they'd found along a number line. "Look," he said, "By arranging the lengths on this number line, we can visually see which logs meet our inequality, $L < 5$. That's a graphical representation of our inequality!"

The others gathered around to examine Leo's drawing.

They marveled at how the inequality translated into a visual graph, making it easier to understand and interpret the condition Thales had set for them.

As they assembled the logs into a raft, they constantly had to keep in mind the inequality condition. This hands-on experience gave them a tangible understanding of inequalities and demonstrated their practical importance. Paddling towards the island, Thales yelled out another task. Two paths, one shorter and one longer, were marked out on the water's surface. To complete the challenge, they were to pick a path that would take more than 10 minutes but less than 20 minutes to navigate.

Priya's mind clicked into place. "This is a compound inequality! If 'T' is the time taken, we're looking at $10 < T < 20$."

A heated discussion started as they calculated their paddling speed and decided which path would satisfy the compound inequality. Just as they were about to set off, Thales yelled out another instruction, "There's a change of plans! Now, the path you choose not only has to satisfy the time constraint but also the speed constraint. You should neither paddle too slow (less than 2 feet per second) nor too fast (more than 5 feet per second). Let's call the speed 'S'. So, you now have two inequalities to satisfy, $2 < S < 5$ and $10 < T < 20$."

"Ah, a system of inequalities!" exclaimed Priya. The friends quickly recalculated their paddling strategy, now having to consider both time and speed. It was a tricky balancing act, but after some teamwork and thinking, they managed to choose a path that satisfied both inequalities.

By the time they reached the island, the sun had begun its descent, casting long shadows over the land. Exhausted but satisfied, they had not only accomplished their challenge but also acquired a profound understanding of inequalities.

As they settled down for the night, their newly built fire crackling merrily, they reflected on their journey. Each realm, each challenge, was a unique lesson in algebra.

They realized that algebra was not just about numbers and symbols. It was a language, a key that unlocked solutions, bridged concepts, and linked math to real-world situations.

As the embers of their fire danced against the starry night sky, they found their thoughts drawn to the journey that was now behind them. They remembered standing in the shadow of the Tower of Exponents, taming the untamed at the Palace of Polynomials, and finding balance in the Twin Cities of Equations.

Each realm held a lesson, a challenge, and a victory. As they saw their own reflections in the flickering flames, they were no longer mere students of Algebra, but explorers who dared to tackle the unknown. Their adventures in the magical realm of algebra had been challenging, but the knowledge they gained was their greatest reward.

CHAPTER 19 OVERVIEW

Concepts Covered

- **COMPOUND INEQUALITIES:** The adventurers learned about compound inequalities, which are two inequalities joined by the words "and" or "or." They discovered how to solve these by separating them into two individual inequalities.
- **GRAPHING INEQUALITIES:** This includes drawing a graph to represent the solutions to an inequality. The adventurers learned how to do this on a number line.
- **SYSTEMS OF INEQUALITIES:** These are multiple inequalities that are solved simultaneously. The adventurers had to solve a system of inequalities to navigate through the Island of Comparison.

Practical Applications

Compound inequalities and systems of inequalities are used in various real-world scenarios, such as determining acceptable ranges of values and making decisions based on multiple constraints.

Key Equations or Formulas

Compound Inequality (AND): $a < x < b$
Compound Inequality (OR): $x < a$ or $x > b$
System of Inequalities: A set of inequalities that must all be satisfied simultaneously.

Practice Problems

1. The mystical inequality squirrels can only climb trees that are taller than 2 meters but shorter than 5 meters. Can you write a compound inequality to represent this?

2. The magical pearl in a game must land somewhere greater than 15 meters but less than 25 meters away. Can you graph this inequality on a number line?

3. For a magical ritual on the island, the temperature 'T' must be above 20 degrees, and the wind speed 'W' should be less than 10 m/s. Write this as a system of inequalities.

4. During a magical contest on the island, a team wins if their score 'S' is more than 10 but less than 20, and if the number of team members 'M' is at least 5 but not more than 10. Write this situation as a system of compound inequalities and graph it.

Solutions

1. The mystical inequality squirrels can climb trees that are taller than 2 meters but shorter than 5 meters. This can be represented by the compound inequality $2 < T < 5$, where T is the tree height.

2. For the magical pearl to land somewhere greater than 15 meters but less than 25 meters away, you can graph this on a number line. Mark a line with two open dots at 15 and 25 and shade the region between them.

3. For the magical ritual on the island, the temperature 'T' must be above 20 degrees, and the wind speed 'W' should be less than 10 m/s. This situation can be written as the system of inequalities $T > 20$, $W < 10$.

4. A team wins if their score 'S' is more than 10 but less than 20, and if the number of team members 'M' is at least 5 but not more than 10. This situation can be written as the system of compound inequalities:

$10 < S < 20$
$5 \leq M \leq 10$

They can be graphed on a coordinate plane with S and M as axes. A rectangular region will be formed between S=10 and S=20 (excluding these lines), and between M=5 and M=10 (including these lines).

Glossary

Algebra: A branch of mathematics that uses symbols or letters to represent numbers, quantities, and relationships between them.

Variable: A symbol, typically a letter, that represents one or more numbers.

Equation: A mathematical statement that asserts the equality of two expressions. It contains an equals sign (=).

Inequality: A mathematical statement that compares two expressions that may not be equal. It uses symbols like < (less than), > (greater than), ≤ (less than or equal to), or ≥ (greater than or equal to).

Polynomial: An algebraic expression made up of terms. The terms consist of variables and coefficients, combined using addition, subtraction, and non-negative integer exponents.

Quadratic Equation: A polynomial equation of the second degree. The general form is $ax^2 + bx + c = 0$, where a, b, and c are constants, and x is a variable.

Linear Equation: A polynomial equation of the first degree. The general form is $ax + b = 0$, where a and b are constants, and x is a variable.

Exponent: The number of times a number or expression (the base) is multiplied by itself.

Fraction: A numerical quantity that is not a whole number, represented by two numbers, the numerator and the denominator.

Function: A rule that relates inputs to outputs in a way that each input corresponds to exactly one output.

Graph: A diagram that shows the relationship between two or more quantities.

System of Equations: A set of two or more equations that have the same variables.

Rational Equation: An equation containing at least one fraction whose numerator or denominator is a variable.

Probability: A measure of the likelihood that a particular event will occur, expressed as a number between 0 and 1.

Data Analysis: The process of evaluating data to reach conclusions or to support decision making.

Inequalities: Mathematical expressions involving the symbols > (greater than), < (less than), ≤ (less than or equal to), or ≥ (greater than or equal to).

Absolute Value: The distance a number is from zero on a number line. Always non-negative.

Compound Inequality: A combination of two or more inequalities joined together by the words "and" or "or".

Coefficient: The numerical factor of a term that contains a variable. In the term 4x, 4 is the coefficient.

Expression: A mathematical phrase that can contain numbers, operators, variables, and/or groupings, such as parentheses.

Index

Hey there Math Master,

You've reached the end of this mathematical adventure! We're really hoping you enjoyed it, and we'd love to hear what you thought.

If you could take a minute to leave a review on whichever platform you bought this book, that would be super helpful. Your thoughts can make a big difference - they help us make our next books even better, and they also help other folks figure out if this book is right for them. So go ahead and let us know what you liked, what made you go "aha!", and what books you'd like to see us release next. We appreciate it!

Here's a little math fun for you - you know, we always say that feedback is like a mathematical constant: it's essential in our journey of constant improvement.

So, thank you for being part of our equation!

OUT NOW

Continue your math adventure
with Geometry Through Stories.
Available now from your Favorite
Online Bookstores

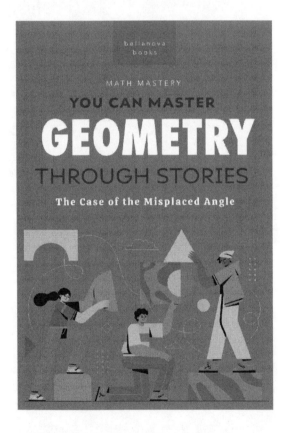

Made in the USA
Middletown, DE
21 May 2024

54659324R00104